NOV 18 1

D0873867

HEAT ENGINES

JOHN F. SANDFORT, who is head of the Mechanical Engineering Department of the South Dakota State College, at Brookings, was introduced to power machinery in a Columbus, Ohio, creamery where his father was chief engineer, and the acquaintance has ripened into an enduring fascination. A graduate of Ohio State University in mechanical and industrial engineering (1933, 1934), he worked for the Frigidaire Division of General Motors and then decided upon teaching as a career. Before joining the South Dakota faculty in 1958, he served four years as an artillery officer in Europe and the Pacific in World War II and did graduate work at the State University of Iowa. His incentive in writing *Heat Engines* was the hope of stimulating more interest, not only in physics but in mechanical engineering as well, a field that is built on the basic science of physics as its cornerstone.

HEAT ENGINES

JOHN F. SANDFORT

PUBLISHED BY ANCHOR BOOKS
DOUBLEDAY & COMPANY, INC.
GARDEN CITY, NEW YORK

621.4
S217

ILLUSTRATIONS BY
ROBERT L. KELLEY

TJ
265
.S25

NOV 6 1970 Cooper Union Library

LIBRARY OF CONGRESS
CATALOG CARD NUMBER 62–14688
COPYRIGHT © 1962 BY
EDUCATIONAL SERVICES INCORPORATED
ALL RIGHTS RESERVED
PRINTED IN THE UNITED STATES OF AMERICA

354065

PREFACE

This book was written with the idea that engineering thermodynamics is not the stodgy and abstruse subject that many suppose, but rather a fascinating science that grew out of a great human need—the production of power from heat. The story of thermodynamics is firmly entwined with the historical development of the heat engine, and library research on this subject reveals many interesting and exciting stories and anecdotes in old books, journals, and transactions. I hope that I have been able to capture at least some of the drama in this seldom-told story.

I am indebted to Dr. H. J. Stoever, a friend and former colleague at Iowa State University, for many effective ideas and ways of presenting this subject. Dr. Stoever is not only an author but also a highly inspirational teacher of thermodynamics, as many of his former students and associates will attest.

In addition I want to thank Professor A. G. Trump, South Dakota State College Librarian, for his help in locating source material, Mrs. Donna Sisk for her skillful typing of the manuscript, and my wife, Lela, for her infinite patience and encouragement during the long hours of preparation.

Finally I want to thank John H. Durston for his most valuable editorial suggestions.

John F. Sandfort

Brookings, South Dakota
December 1961

CONTENTS

CONTENTS

THE SCIENCE
STUDY SERIES

The Science Study Series offers to students and to the general public the writing of distinguished authors on the most stirring and fundamental topics of science, from the smallest known particles to the whole universe. Some of the books tell of the role of science in the world of man, his technology and civilization. Others are biographical in nature, telling the fascinating stories of the great discoverers and their discoveries. All the authors have been selected both for expertness in the fields they discuss and for ability to communicate their special knowledge and their own views in an interesting way. The primary purpose of these books is to provide a survey within the grasp of the young student or the layman. Many of the books, it is hoped, will encourage the reader to make his own investigations of natural phenomena.

The Series, which now offers topics in all the sciences and their applications, had its beginning in a project to revise the secondary schools' physics curriculum. At the Massachusetts Institute of Technology during 1956 a group of physicists, high school teachers, journalists, apparatus designers, film producers, and other specialists organized the Physical Science Study Committee, now operating as a part of Educational Services Incorporated, Watertown, Massachusetts. They pooled their knowledge and experience toward the design and creation of aids to the learning of physics. Initially their effort was supported by the National Science Foundation, which has continued to aid the program. The Ford Foundation, the Fund for the Advancement of Education, and the Alfred P. Sloan Foundation have also given support. The Committee has created a textbook, an extensive film series, a laboratory guide, especially designed apparatus, and a teachers' source book.

The Series is guided by a Board of Editors, consisting of Bruce F. Kingsbury, Managing Editor; John H. Durston, General Editor; Paul F. Brandwein, the Conservation Foundation and Harcourt, Brace & World, Inc.; Francis L. Friedman, Massachusetts Institute of Technology; Samuel A. Goudsmit, Brookhaven National Laboratory; Philippe LeCorbeiller, Harvard University; and Gerard Piel, *Scientific American*.

INTRODUCTION

Man is an earth-bound animal, of only average size, and physically weak as animals go, yet he dominates the earth. As a matter of fact, he has loosened the shackles of the earth's great gravitational field and moved in the new frontiers of outer space. How has this come about? It happened because man discovered the vast reservoirs of energy available to him on earth and learned how to control them. Unlocking this secret has made possible the remarkable growth of our modern technological civilization. It is the key that has turned certain nations into great military powers and has made possible the highest standard of living of all time.

Behind these accomplishments of the past and the mighty achievements still to come lies the epoch of power, and in this world of power the heat engine, a device for converting heat to work, continues to reign supreme.

Prior to the 18th century the inanimate heat engine[1] was unknown except as a toy or curiosity.

---

[1] All animals are heat engines in the sense that they convert low temperature heat energy (metabolism) into muscular work.

Then suddenly the first crude heat engines began to appear as useful power machines. They were built by engineers with no formal technical education, because at the time engineering colleges did not exist. But those men were avid and persistent, and they sought out the meager information in mathematics and the physical sciences that the mathematician and the physicist of that day were able to give. Still, for 150 years the heat engine developed very slowly because there was no fundamental theory or understanding of the energy and forces with which it operated.

Then, in the middle of the 19th century, a very small group of mathematical and experimental physicists, in a brilliant burst of creative effort seldom seen in the history of science, formulated the theory of heat, work, and energy, on the foundation of the First and Second Laws of Thermodynamics. With this new science of thermodynamics and with the deeper knowledge supplied by schools of engineering and technology, the engineers have brought the heat engine to its present high state of development. This is the story that we shall try to tell.

For uncounted centuries man depended on muscular power, wind power, and water power, to harvest and prepare food and clothing, to control to some degree the environment around him, and to transport things from place to place. Until comparatively recent times the fastest man could travel was on the back of a horse. Beasts of burden were domesticated to help perform many heavy and oppressive tasks.

The energy in the wind was recognized early as a potential source of power, and was used around the earth to drive sailing ships. In Europe, by the 10th century A.D., the wind was being harnessed, through windmills, to pump water and grind grain. Water power was used much earlier as a source of mechanical power to drive mechanical devices, usually grain mills. The weight of falling water was utilized, through a variety of water wheels, to provide a steady and dependable power source.

These primitive forms of power are still in use in certain areas of the world today. Primitive water wheels can be found, and beasts of burden remain the prime source of power in some backward countries. Fantastic as it seems to us in America today, there are still major areas of the world where vast hordes of human beings labor to build dams, roads, and dikes, and undertake other large earth-moving projects, with no other tools than hand shovels, picks, and baskets. And the price these countries pay for this state of affairs is reflected in human misery, drudgery, and periodic famine.

It is evident to us now that our modern civilization could never have evolved had we been content merely to refine and perfect the machines that used these primitive power sources. The Yankee clippers, with their clean lines and superb performance, represented the ultimate in the evolution of commercial sailing vessels. Yet their sailing schedules were limited by the velocity and dependability of the trade winds. The strength and speed of draft animals are limited by nature, and a highly developed water wheel could never be used to pump out a flooded mine shaft if a source of water power did not happen to be near the mine. For a long time men searched for a source of power that would be portable, reliable, highly concentrated, and easily controlled. But before this could come about, a major breakthrough in human knowledge was necessary.

As is true of most fundamental concepts, energy is something difficult to define and comprehend. It is obvious to everyone that it takes energy to carry a heavy load up a steep hill. It should also be obvious that energy is associated somehow with a falling rock, and that these two forms of energy should somehow be related. It is not quite so obvious, however, that energy also is involved in boiling a pail of water, or that there should be any connection between these phenomena.

A few curious men around the start of the 19th century did wonder about these vague connections, however, and they began to perform simple experiments and record their observations. Just what was this mysterious phenomenon that might appear from burning fuel, rubbing objects together, or even directly from the rays of the sun?

The earliest attempts to describe the nature of heat involved the caloric theory. According to this theory the manifestations of heat were due to the action of a fluid called caloric, which had the power to penetrate and expand all substances or to dissolve certain materials into a vapor. This theory seemed reasonable enough and accounted for most of the observable facts regarding heat, temperature, and combustion. It is true that no one was able to determine the weight of this caloric fluid as bodies were heated and cooled. As a matter of fact, attempts were made, but no reproducible results could be obtained. However, this failure was explained by assuming that the caloric could not be detected with the instruments and experimental techniques of the day.

Nevertheless, a few stubborn men were not satisfied. Incongruous observations kept popping up that could not be explained by the caloric theory. For example, it was observed that gases had a temperature rise when compressed, and bearing surfaces became hot when not properly lubricated. The caloric theorists insisted that the heat of friction could be explained as a loss of caloric fluid, when caloric was squeezed or ground out of a material. However, this explanation was demonstrated to be inadequate as early as 1798 in a famous cannon-boring experiment in a Bavarian arsenal. Count Rumford (1753–1814) formulated the strategy and directed the action.

Rumford was a most remarkable man. He was born Benjamin Thompson in Woburn, Massachusetts, and received only a limited technical education. This was in revolutionary times, and since Rumford's sympathies were with the Tories, he found it expedient to move to England. There he proved to have unusual abilities as an organizer and scientific experimenter, and was honored by King George III. He was a restless adventurer, however, and soon moved again, this time to Europe. He began working for the Elector of Bavaria as Chamberlain, Minister of War, and Minister of Police. He reorganized the army and as a reward received the title of Count of the Holy Roman Empire.

During this period he continued his scientific experimentation in spite of his many other duties, and one day in 1798, while he was supervising the operation of his cannon-boring mill, a great idea came to him. But let us hear it in his own words:

> Being engaged, lately, in superintending the boring of cannon, in the workshops of the military arsenal at Munich, I was struck with the very considerable degree of Heat which a brass gun acquires in a short time, in being bored; and with the still more intense Heat (much greater than that of boiling water, as I found by experiment) of the metallic chips separated from it by the borer.

> The more I meditated on these phaenomena, the more they appeared to me to bid fair to give a farther insight into the hidden nature of Heat; and to enable us to form some reasonable conjectures respecting the existence, or non-existence, of an igneous fluid: a subject on which the opinions of philosophers have, in all ages, been much divided.

Rumford proceeded to set up experiments to measure the quantity of heat produced in this operation. He built a vat around a cannon barrel, filled the vat with water and, while horses turned the mill, measured how long it took for the process of boring to raise the water to the boiling point. From his observations he concluded that the supply of heat must be limitless. This was indeed a revolutionary concept, not at all acceptable to the proponents of the caloric theory. They pointed out that the large quantity of heat released was due to the great pressure produced by the boring tool, which was squeezing out caloric, and they insisted that an accurate measurement of the heat capacity of the bored-out material would probably verify this contention. However, when Rumford measured the heat capacity of the chips, he found it to be identical with that of the parent material.

Using a very accurate analytical balance, Count Rumford made additional careful experiments to try to measure the "weight of heat." He compared the weight of water, both before and after freezing, but he could never find a measurable difference. He decided that further experimentation along this line would always prove negative, and finally he came to the following remarkable conclusion:

It is hardly necessary to add that anything which any insulated body, or system of bodies, can continue to furnish without limitation, cannot possibly be a material substance: and it appears to me to be extremely difficult, if not quite impossible, to form any distinct idea of anything capable of being excited or communicated, in the manner the Heat was excited and communicated in these Experiments, except it be MOTION.

Rumford's experiments shook the foundations of the caloric theory but could not topple it. Nevertheless, his conclusion set other scientists to wondering. Just a year after the famous cannon-boring experiment, the great English chemist Sir Humphry Davy, then only 21 years old, performed some experiments that were a more direct refutation of the caloric theory. He set up an apparatus, with a remote-control mechanism, whereby he could rub substances together in a vacuum. He tried both ice and wax, and according to the prevalent theory the rubbing action should have squeezed caloric *out* of the substances. The results of his experiments were contradictory to the theory, however. The ice and the wax melted, and only *addition* of caloric to the substance could explain this.

Davy's experiments intensified doubt of the validity of the intricate theories of the Calorists, and gradually, out of this early probing into the true nature of heat, came a better understanding of energy. The mechanical theory of heat was proposed, and there was a persistent feeling that somehow heat and work were interrelated. This was a dramatic point in history. Underneath the earth's crust lay vast but unsuspected stores of the fossil fuels—coal, oil, and gas. The deposits of fissionable fuels were also there, but their potential use was not even dreamed of. Here were concentrated energy sources available for the taking. Here was the answer to man's search for mechanical power if he could but unravel the riddle of heat, work, and energy.

We know now that the riddle was solved

(though many more complex problems that remain to be solved were introduced in the process). The work of a few experimental physicists, culminating in the precise experiments of James P. Joule (1818–1889), established beyond all doubt that heat and work are only different manifestations of the same thing, energy. We shall see in later chapters exactly how this came about. It was postulated that although heat-energy and work-energy can each be changed into the other form, energy itself can never be created nor destroyed. A second remarkable hypothesis evolved when it became clear that the particular conversion of heat to work is unique in that it never can be complete. In other words, only a certain maximum percentage of any source of heat energy can be converted into work and power, even though work can always be completely converted into heat.

Other puzzling aspects of this subject began to clear up. The true nature and significance of temperature became recognized, and a thermodynamic scale of temperature became established. The interplay of heat and work, acting on fluid systems, was studied both in theory and in the laboratory, and other important properties of gases, liquids, and solids were identified. Out of this activity emerged a new discipline, the science of thermodynamics, and out of thermodynamics emerged the heat engine, which in its many forms completely dominates the enormous power resources available to and used by man today.

We tend to take this all for granted, and so perhaps it would be helpful to examine some statistics, to understand and better appreciate the magnitude of this explosive increase in the production and application of power.

An average man can produce muscular work continuously at the rate of about $\frac{1}{20}$ horsepower. This is about 37 watts when converted to electrical energy units, or 71 kilowatt hours per year, working 8 hours per day for 240 equivalent working days per year. Statistics from the Edison Electric Institute show that there were 17,314 kilowatt hours of electrical energy used for each worker employed in American industry in 1954. Assuming that electricity accounts for 95 per cent of all power used in industry, we see that mechanical power equivalent to 257 men supplemented the efforts of each worker.

The operating engineer of a modern plant of 1,000,000 horsepower routinely controls the equivalent power of 20 million men by simply closing a few switches. The average family in the United States uses more than 2600 kilowatt hours of electricity per year to operate lights, washing machines, vacuum cleaners, furnaces, air conditioners, refrigerators, etc. Add to this consumption a 150-horsepower automobile, and we are startled to see that our family is served by the energy equivalent of a labor force of 37 men, and that they have at their command the power of 3000 men to move them from place to place. And all this power is concentrated in small packages, easily controlled, instantly available.

In the following chapters we shall see how the science of thermodynamics was developed, and how the various types of heat engines evolved. It may seem at times that the development of heat engines and thermodynamics proceeded along parallel but independent paths. In fact, the earliest steam engines were used for over a century before thermodynamics was developed as a formal organized body of knowledge. Furthermore, they were often built and utilized by ingenious men, called engineers, who had little or no formal, advanced scientific training. Men like James Watt, Oliver Evans, and Robert Fulton seemed to have an obsession for inventing, innovating, and developing new machines and devices, useful to mankind, that could be manufactured and sold for a profit. In this respect these engineers differed from the scientists who worked in the universities and laboratories, seeking new knowledge about our physical world and expanding and refining the various disciplines in basic science and mathematics.

Nevertheless, it is true that in the larger sense the heat engine evolved out of the science of thermodynamics. The early engineers, working with materials, forces, and processes which they never really understood, were forced to rely on trial-and-error procedures and empirical data and relationships in the design of their engines. This groping in the dark was painfully slow progress. The engines were primitive and crude, heavy and ponderous, and they operated at very low efficiencies. The engineer's ingenuity and a flair for inventiveness were certainly necessary, but they were not sufficient qualifications in themselves to bring the heat engine to its full potentiality. The development of thermodynamics, and to a lesser extent other engineering sciences, gave the engineer the theoretical tools that showed him the possibilities and limitations within which he must work. It made possible an analytical approach by which he could drive straight to the heart of the problem without the costly, time-consuming guesswork of trial and error.

The heat engines and other prime movers of the future will be designed and developed by mechanical engineers who have a strong foundation in mathematics, the basic sciences of chemistry and physics, and the specific engineering sciences applying to this field. These men will be engineers who have completed a serious and purposeful college education. They will meet the scientists on a common ground and speak with them in a common language.

HEAT ENGINES

CHAPTER 1

PRIMITIVE HEAT ENGINES

A *heat engine* is defined in the dictionary as an engine that converts the energy of heat into mechanical energy; a *prime mover* is any naturally occurring agency that has been applied by man to the production of power. Although there are many different classes of prime movers such as draft animals, water turbines, windmills, tide machines, and battery-operated motors, the heat engine is by far the most important and versatile of all the present-day prime movers. It enjoys this supremacy because heat sources in the form of fuels have been abundantly available throughout the earth in highly concentrated forms. *Thermodynamics,* which goes back only about 100 years, is the science that interprets the relationship between heat and work and makes possible an understanding of the processes, systems, and machines by which heat and work can be interchanged.

Long before the principles of thermodynamics were formulated, a few men made attempts to build heat engines. Some of these contraptions were mere laboratory curiosities. Others were built for the specific purpose of doing a particular job, such as pumping water. All were primitive by mod-

Fig. 1. Hero's aeolipile

ern standards. They were built by men who observed certain forces and motions that occurred when heat was applied to water and air.

Ancient writing on this subject establishes the fact that heat engines were described and small models built in Greece in the centuries before and after the birth of Christ. These devices, however cleverly contrived, were nothing more than toys, and in some cases were built specifically for this purpose. The most famous device to come out of Greece was Hero's aeolipile, probably built about 75 A.D. It consisted of a hollow metal sphere, supported between two horizontal bearings above a brazier where a fire could be kindled. Two bent tubes were fastened to the sphere in such a way that when the sphere was filled with steam under pressure, the steam would flow in opposite directions from the bent tubes and cause the sphere to rotate (Fig. 1). It was a simple device that any high school student can duplicate with a tin can spinning between two nails, a bit of 1/4-inch copper tubing, and a Bunsen burner.

Hero could not have understood why his aeolipile acted as it did, and, to our knowledge, made no attempt to employ it in any useful manner. It took about 1900 years for man to understand what caused Hero's sphere to turn. Isaac Newton stated the principle in his Third Law of Motion: "To every action there is an equal and opposite reaction." In other words, the turning sphere is merely the reaction caused by the change of momentum due to the speeding up of the steam in expanding through the *moving* nozzles. Turbines that operate on this principle are now known as *reaction turbines*. It took another hundred years to understand that heat energy was being converted into kinetic energy in the steam blowing from the nozzles, but after the theory was completely devel-

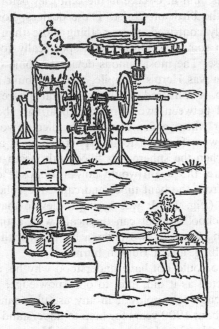

Fig. 2. Branca's steam turbine

oped, it took only 50 years more to convert this toy into useful work-producing reaction steam turbines. Descendants of these turbines are the mighty prime movers that drive generators in our modern power plants today.

In 1629 Giovanni Branca conceived the idea of an *impulse* turbine, which was intended to power a pounding machine through crude wooden gears, Fig. 2. It is interesting to note that his turbine worked on a different principle from Hero's turbine. In this principle the steam acquires a high velocity by expanding to a lower pressure in a *stationary* nozzle. This high velocity steam then strikes against moving turbine blades where its direction is changed and its velocity is decreased. The momentum of the steam decreases, and the blades experience an impulse. The resulting force causes the turbine to rotate and do work. Turbines designed in this manner today are called impulse turbines. It is not certain that Branca's machine was ever built, but in all probability it was not. It is easy to see that the friction and other losses would have been so great that little or no useful work could have resulted. It was significant, though, that the idea was becoming established that somehow fire and water could be put together to produce useful work.

Water Pumps

One of the most burdensome tasks that have faced man since the earliest civilizations has been the raising and transporting of large quantities of water. Then, as now, large amounts of water were necessary for the various functions of community living, and as men began to dig deep into the earth to mine valuable ores, they engaged in frequent struggles with underground water flooding the pits.

We know that water pumps were in use long before 1600. There were many ingenious designs, including multiple buckets, ball and chain, Archi-

Fig. 3. A "four-horsepower" pump for draining a mine

medean screws, and suction pumps. One elaborate installation was constructed at Chemnitz, in what is now East Germany, around 1550. It consisted of four main pumps of the ball-and-chain design and lifted water 660 feet in three stages. Ninety-six horses in teams of eight, working four hours and resting twelve, operated the pump. Another design used about 1615 (Fig. 3) employed four horses in an unsuccessful attempt to drain a mine. It is not astonishing that the amount of water pumped was small, due to friction and other losses, and it is interesting to compare the size of this cumbersome apparatus to a typical standard model centrifugal pump of today. A 3-horsepower pump can lift 250 gallons per minute through a vertical distance of 25 feet while occupying a floor space of only 40 inches by 15 inches.

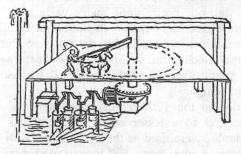

Fig. 4. Four-cylinder pump showing rotary to reciprocating motion

Another significant design was proposed in 1589 (Fig. 4), in which a 4-cylinder suction pump employed a crankshaft for converting rotary motion into reciprocating motion. The use of pistons, moving back and forth with a reciprocating action in a cylinder and turning a flywheel through a crank, is an arrangement as familiar to us as our automobile, whose engine employs such a mechanism. However, the principle was not always so obvious. There is some evidence that the Greeks had invented the piston and cylinder before 200 B.C. Much later the idea of a crankshaft appeared. These mechanisms were all associated with *pumping machines,* but few models were actually built, probably because of the difficulty of building to sufficiently close tolerances. In retrospect, it seems strange that the idea of using the cylinder, piston, and crank for changing the reciprocating motion of the early *steam engines* to the more convenient rotary motion should have taken so long to root. As we shall see later, this idea did not occur until many years after the steam engine had become an important commercial machine. In fact, English patents were granted for this mechanism, as applied to a heat engine, 200 years after they were proposed for use on pump designs.

Prior to the 17th century only men and animals, and to a lesser extent water wheels and windmills, were used as the prime movers for water pumps. Here was a real human need requiring large concentrations of power capable of being applied over long periods of time. The economic incentives were present to encourage the engineers of that time in experimentation. Water was a necessity of life.

As far back as the Hellenistic times, Ctesibius and Hero investigated and made notes on the properties of steam. These writings may have had some influence on later investigations on the subject, but it was not until 1601 that Giambattista della Porta observed that water could be made to rise in a chamber if one first filled the chamber with steam and then condensed the vapor. Others observed the same phenomenon, and in 1630 David Ramsay received a patent in Scotland for "An Apparatus to Raise Water from Lowe Pitts by Fire." However, nothing more is known about the device. In 1659 Robert Thornton, from an English coal mining district, experimented with the suction lift of liquids, and established the theoretical height that water could be lifted by suction pump. In his own words, "two foot and a half and some odd inches of a tube of quicksilver, equiponderates with 32 feet of water—betwixt the Earth and atmosphere." On this information he designed a device for lifting water with a vacuum formed by condensing steam. Thus Thornton probably was one of the first men to describe a heat engine in detail, although a number of other designs were proposed about the same time.

In this period scientists began systematic investigations of the properties of air and water. Evangelista Torricelli and Blaise Pascal had developed the barometer in 1643, by inverting a tube of mercury sealed at the top. This discovery probably influenced Thornton and other engineers in developing the idea of a suction-lift pump somewhat later. In 1654 Otto von Guericke, in Germany, invented the reciprocating air vacuum pump, using the old piston and cylinder principle. He dramatized his invention in a famous demonstration at Magdeburg, in which he evacuated the air from two close-fitting hemispheres and showed that 16 horses could not pull them apart. It was the pressure of the atmosphere, of course, that held the hemispheres together. The vacuum pump opened the way for investigations of the properties of air and steam under vacuum. Sir Samuel Morland (1625–1695) was the first to prepare tables that showed how the boiling temperature of water varied with pressure. Robert Boyle (1627–1691) experimented with the "Spring of the Air," and history has given his name to the following law, which later became one of the basics of thermodynamics: "For a given temperature, the volume of a gas varies inversely as the pressure exerted on it." A few other scientists began investigating certain physical constants and physical properties of matter. Although this information was incomplete and often inaccurate, it did give the engineers of that time some basis on which to proceed with steam engine design.

We should not overlook the development in mathematics that also occurred at this time. The Frenchman René Descartes (1596–1650) discovered analytical geometry, which facilitated a better understanding of the relationship between mathematical variables and laid the geometrical foundation for calculus. Sir Isaac Newton (1642–1727), one of the greatest scientists of all times, invented* the differential calculus, the branch of

* Gottfried Wilhelm Leibniz, German lawyer and philosopher, developed and published the calculus without knowledge of Newton's earlier but unpublished work.

mathematics that deals with the rates at which variables change. Newton also made monumental contributions to mechanics, culminating in his three basic laws of motion. An understanding of basic mechanics was essential in the subsequent evolution of the steam engine. This understanding permitted at least some sort of intelligent and economical utilization of materials in the design of component parts such as cylinders, pistons, connecting rods, crankshafts, cams, valves, gears, and flywheels.

Savery's Fire Engine

With the accelerating interest and increased experimentation in this field, by both scientists and engineers, it was inevitable that some form of practical heat engine would soon appear. The first man to produce one was Thomas Savery, an English engineer (1650–1715), who obtained a patent in 1698 for a machine (Fig. 5) designed to drain water from mines. He called his machine a "fire engine," because fire generated the steam for its operation.

The machine contained no moving parts except hand-operated steam valves and automatic check valves, and in principle it worked as follows. Steam was generated in a spherical boiler and admitted to a separate vessel where it expelled much of the air. The steam valve then was closed and cold water allowed to flow over the vessel, causing the steam to condense and thus creating a

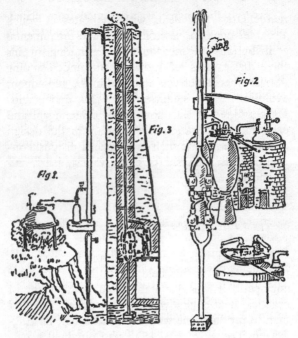

Fig. 5. Savery's steam pump

partial vacuum. This vacuum pulled water into the vessel from the area to be drained. Then, by a further operation of valves, steam was readmitted to the vessel to force the water through a vertical pipe to the discharge elevation. Thus, by a successive manipulation of valves, this apparatus could pump water in a continuous manner, operating at about five cycles[1] per minute.

[1] A cycle is a sequence of operations whereby various processes are performed and the machine is brought back to its starting point ready to start another identical sequence.

Savery's fire engine was designed from principles, knowledge, and observations reported by others. He made use of Torricelli's vacuum and della Porta's observed suction lift. He employed Thornton's condensing technique and added some original ideas of his own, and finally obtained his patent. Then, after he designed his first prototype model, he did something that had never been done before with a heat engine. He obtained financial backing and set up a factory in London in 1702 for the manufacture of his engine. He promoted its sale through systematic advertising and by demonstrating its superiority over animal-operated pumps.

Savery's apparatus was enormously wasteful of fuel, but neither he nor anyone else cared, fuel then being cheap. Here was a device that used fire (heat) to raise water (do useful work), but no one really understood what was happening. For example, Savery could not test his engine to measure its efficiency. In fact, efficiency had no meaning to him. He could have no concept that energy was being converted from one form to another, that a certain percentage of the heating value of the coal was being changed into the mechanical work necessary to lift the water through a vertical distance. If you could have asked Mr. Savery to describe the operation of his engine, he would have used such expressions as "incensed and inflamed air," "intercourse of the two contraries," and "frustrated ascent of water," amusing fancies but meaningless today.

Nevertheless, Savery's fire engine was a financial success. Word got around that here was an engine that would do something that teams of horses could not do. Flooded mines could now be reopened. The Age of Steam was at hand, the Industrial Revolution about to start, and in the brief time of a couple of centuries the profound effect on our civilization would compare with the combined contributions of the Stone Age, the Bronze Age, and the Iron Age, each of which took thousands of years to evolve.

CHAPTER 2

HEAT ENGINE PROGRESS FROM SAVERY TO CARNOT

We said that Savery's commercial "fire engine" ushered in the Age of Steam, but historians prefer to call this era the Industrial Revolution. It was, indeed, a period of intense industrialization in England and Western Europe. The population increased rapidly. Great Britain created its great colonial empire and became the unchallenged mistress of the seas. Whatever the cause of this dynamic technological development, this much is clear: it could not have proceeded without the heat engine to supply the insatiable need for horsepower.

Newcomen's Steam Engine

Ten years after Savery built his fire engine factory, another heat engine appeared that was destined to quickly replace the "fire engine" as a pump and prime mover. This was a steam engine designed and built by Thomas Newcomen (1663–1729) and his partner, John Calley.

Newcomen was born in Dartmouth, England. Besides being an engineer, he pursued the careers

HEAT ENGINES

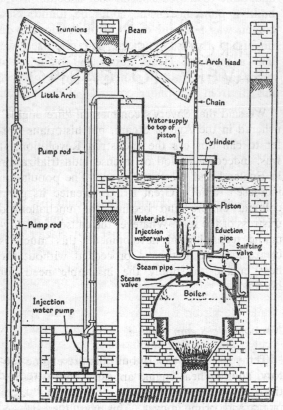

Fig. 6. Newcomen's pumping engine

16

of ironmonger and preacher. He was nearly forty years old when he began studying Savery's engine and came to the conclusion that a better way to build a pumping engine could be found. Newcomen was a friend of Dr. Robert Hooke, distinguished English physicist, and discussed with him a proposal Denis Papin had made, some years earlier, to obtain motive power by exhausting air from a cylinder equipped with a piston. Newcomen wanted to try using steam to produce the vacuum in a manner similar to that suggested earlier by della Porta and successfully followed by Savery in his fire engine. It was Newcomen's idea to have a steam-induced vacuum draw down the piston in the cylinder, and thus produce a straight-line reciprocating motion that could be transferred to a pump through a suitable linkage.

Calley, who was a plumber and glazier, built the engine in 1712 to Newcomen's plans and specifications. It is illutrated in Fig. 6.

The boiler was taken from an old brewers' kettle and was valved to admit steam to the cylinder while the piston was moving toward the top end of its stroke. The admission of this steam prevented air from accumulating in the cylinder under the piston. Next, the steam valve was closed and cold water was sprayed directly into the cylinder to condense the steam. This injection gave a much more effective cooling action than Savery's arrangement of having the condensing water flow around the *outside* of the steam vessel. The resulting vacuum was below the piston, which, under pressure of the atmosphere on top, now descended into the vacuum. (Hence this engine was sometimes referred to as an atmospheric engine.) Note the small pipe supplying water to the top of the piston in Fig. 6. The water provided a more effective seal between the piston and cylinder wall than could be obtained by a mechanical fit of the parts alone. The descending piston pulled up the pump rod through the action of a walking beam, so constructed with arch heads as circular arcs to permit both piston rod and pump rod to move in straight lines. At the bottom of the piston stroke the water injection valve was shut off and the steam valve reopened. In this way the vacuum was broken, and the weight of the pump rod raised the piston; the cylinder refilled with steam at atmospheric pressure, thus completing the cycle.

This engine had a 21-inch cylinder, 7 feet 10 inches high, and made 12 strokes per minute. When placed in service, it raised 50 gallons of water per minute from a depth of 156 feet.

There are some significant things to point out regarding this engine. The use of a cylinder and piston was a real advance. By this device, a heat engine could be built in which the output was a mechanical force that could be applied to pumping water, or for *other* service. In other words, this was a much more versatile prime mover than Savery's fire engine.

Newcomen could not break away from the idea of using steam to produce a vacuum and letting the atmosphere provide the motive force. He was certainly aware that steam could be generated at higher temperatures and pressures, but he had no reason to believe that causing steam to "push" a piston should result in burning less coal than using it to "pull" a piston. He also may have been influenced by the appealing feature of having the boiler generate steam at atmospheric pressure. Such a boiler was cheaper to build, easier to design, and safer to operate than higher pressure boilers. Had he known at that time (as we shall see later) that there were great theoretical advantages to utilizing the steam at higher *temperatures,* his engine might have taken an entirely different design. As it was, nearly seventy years elapsed before another engineer happened to hit on the advantage of operating the boiler at higher pressures and temperatures.

In order to get a better appreciation of the era in which this early heat engine made its appearance, it is helpful to read the following account that appeared in John Theophilus Desagulier's *Experimental Philosophy,* second volume, 1744.

About the year 1710 Thomas Newcomen, iron monger and John Calley, a glazier, of Dartmouth, in the county of Southampton made then several experiments in private, and having brought their engine to work with a piston, etc., in the latter end of the year 1711 made proposals to draw the water at Griff, in Worwichshire; but their invention meeting not with reception, in March following, thro' the acquaintence of Mr. Potter of Bransgrove, in Worchestershire, they bargained to draw water for Mr. Bock of Wolverhampton, where, after a great many laborius attempts, they did

19

make the engine work; but not being either philosophers to understand the reasons, or mathematicians enough to calculate the powers and to proportion the parts, very luckily by accident found what they sought for.

The lucky accidents that Desagulier referred to were the injection of water in the cylinder, as opposed to Savery's less efficient method, and the control technique that made the engine self-acting. Desagulier went on:

> The engine was rendered self-acting by the ingenuity of Humphrey Potter, a boy employed to mind the engine, who contrived a series of catches and strings worked from the beam, by which the several valves were opened and closed in due order.

The accuracy of Desagulier's account was questioned in later years, but it was certainly representative of the engineering techniques of that day. Engineering mechanics, to be based on Newton's monumental laws, had hardly begun to evolve, and thermodynamics was not to appear until more than a hundred years later. We can only marvel at Newcomen's ingenuity.

Newcomen's engine was an instant success, and he began making arrangements for its manufacture. He decided not to apply for a patent since he was uncertain as to its validity. Savery's patent was quite broad in scope and had recently been extended by special act of Parliament. Instead, he joined the Savery firm and, upon Savery's death in 1715, formed a company to take over the remaining patent rights. Newcomen's company thus controlled the manufacture of steam engines in England until 1733.

The use of the heat engine as an important commercial and industrial prime mover was now firmly established for the first time. Manufacturing and sales promotion proceeded apace. It is interesting to note the following advertisement of Newcomen's engine that appeared in the *London Gazette* of August 1716.

Whereas the invention for raising water by the impellant force of fire, authorized by parliament, is lately brought to the greatest perfection, and all sorts of mines, etc., may be thereby drained and water raised to any height with more ease and less charge than by any other methods hither-to used, as is sufficiently demonstrated by diverse engines of this invention now at work in the several counties of Stafford, Worwich, Cornwall and Flint. These are, therefore to give notice that if any person shall be desirous to treat with the proprietors for such engines, attendance will be given for that purpose every Wednesday at the Sword Blade Coffee House in Birchin Lane, London. . . .

Flooding from underground water had knocked out many of the British coal mines. This wonderful new pumping engine brought one mine after another back into production and virtually saved this important industry. As Newcomen gained manufacturing and operating experience, the size of his engines gradually increased, and they began

21

to appear in applications other than mine drainage. In 1739 a Newcomen engine was built to pump water from a French coal mine 90 feet below the earth's surface. The cylinder had a 30-inch bore, and the piston made a 9-foot stroke and operated at 15 strokes per minute. The capacity of this engine was not recorded, but it was reported to have done in forty-eight hours the work that had previously been done in a week by fifty men and twenty horses working twenty-four hours per day in shifts.

Textile mills, iron works, and ore smelters needed power to operate machinery. However, the reciprocating back-and-forth motion of the walking beam system presented a real problem. Most of the power needs for these other applications called for rotating motion to turn shafts, millstones, lathes, windlasses, etc. It seems odd that it took so many years to work out a design for converting reciprocating motion to rotary motion in a steam engine. Years earlier, mechanisms had been developed for changing the rotary motion of water wheels and windmills into reciprocating motion for pumps, but apparently these inventors had difficulty applying the concept to the early steam engines. The fundamentals of energy were not clearly understood, and the idea of using the energy of a heavy rotating flywheel to obtain a smooth flow of rotary power was not apparent. In the light of present-day knowledge, it seems absurd that many installations were made in which the Newcomen engine was used to pump water up

22

to overhead tanks for use in operating water wheels to provide the desired rotary motion.

The basic patents under which the Newcomen company operated expired in 1733. Soon other steam engine companies were formed to exploit the growing demand for power, both in England and on the Continent. Engineers were encouraged to experiment, modify, and refine existing designs. The zenith of development of the Newcomen engine was probably reached under John Smeaton (1724–1792), versatile English engineer. Smeaton did not actually make any fundamental improvements on the steam engine, but rather brought its original design concept to a high state of perfection, within the limitations of the available manufacturing techniques of that period. The cylinders of his engines were more accurately bored, the pistons more accurately fitted, and the parts more carefully proportioned and balanced. In 1775 Smeaton was commissioned by Catherine II of Russia to build one of his largest engines to pump out the water from the dry docks at the fortress of Kronstadt. This was a gigantic task that previously required a year to accomplish by means of windmills 100 feet high. Smeaton's engine did the job in two weeks.

Smeaton was the first to call himself a "civilian" engineer or "civil" engineer for short, as opposed to the "military" engineers of that day. Prior to his time, engineering was only a vaguely defined occupation. It was recognized as a full-time occupation in France as early as the 17th century, although the first civilian engineering school was not established there until 1747, with the founding of the Ecole des Ponts et Chaussées. It was at this school that the idea of a formal engineering curriculum first appeared, although not in the form we know today. An organized teaching staff was used, and lectures on theoretical subjects were given, but for many years the apprentice system remained the conventional way to train "engineers," by whatever name they were called.

In the early part of the 19th century a number of engineering schools were organized in Europe, particularly in Germany, foremost among them the Ecole Polytechnique, in Paris. The curricula included courses in mathematics, the basic sciences of physics and chemistry, and the various engineering sciences as they became established. The breakdown of curricula into the various branches of engineering such as "Mechanical," "Electrical," "Civil," etc., came later.

The first generally recognized definition of engineering was given by a British architect, Thomas Tredgold, in 1828. He defined it as "the art of directing the great sources of power in nature for the use and convenience of man." This definition was used in the charter of the first technical engineering society. It is interesting to note that this definition clearly recognized the dominant position of the heat engine in the technology of the world during that period.

The Era of James Watt

Eleven years before Smeaton built his great engine for the Kronstadt dry docks, a Glasgow man, then twenty-eight years of age, was called on to try to repair a Newcomen engine that belonged to the University of Glasgow, but had never worked properly. This young man's title was Mathematical Instrument Maker for the University, and his name was James Watt. His experimentation with the Glasgow University engine quickly led to the discovery of basic improvements which were as significant as Newcomen's improvements over the Savery "fire engine." Watt's discoveries were remarkable inasmuch as they came in a period when the state of science and technology had not advanced much beyond the time of Savery and Newcomen. Perfection of the steam engine had to await a satisfactory theory of heat, and Watt's day, remember, was still a generation before Count Rumford and Humphry Davy made the first assaults on the caloric theory. As a matter of fact, the caloric theory was just in its formulation stage at this time, and much of the theoretical and experimental work was being done at the same University of Glasgow where Watt was employed.

For thousands of years man had revered fire. Fire cooked his food and provided warmth and protection against the cold. Its importance was recognized by the early Greeks, who divided all terrestrial matter into four elements, Fire, Air, Water, and Earth, with Fire holding the highest place of all. Although heat was a common phenomenon, observable to all, no progress was made toward its fundamental understanding until the advent of the Scientific Revolution in the 16th century. It was during this period that the concept of temperature appeared, and thermometers were developed to measure the relative "coldness" of things. Joseph Black (1728–1799), Professor of Chemistry at the University of Glasgow, used these thermometers to study the phenomenon of heat, and noticed the tendency of all matter at different temperatures to come to equilibrium when placed together. He studied the phase changes in matter as heat "flowed" in and out, and stated that "all liquids may be considered as solids melted by heat."

Out of investigations such as Black's it was logical that a theory would evolve postulating the existence of an ethereal invisible fluid that flowed in and out of substances and changed their temperature. The theory was originally based on two postulates: (1) that heat fluid could not be created or destroyed, and (2) that the amount of heat fluid transferred to or from an object was proportional to the mass of the object and its change in temperature.

This theory was quite plausible and seemed to be in complete agreement with experimental results. The leading physicists and mathematicians of the time were attracted to it. Antoine Lavoisier, the great French chemist who had overthrown the phlogiston theory of combustion, put the full weight of his prestige behind this new concept of a "heat fluid" and was, in fact, the one who first called it "caloric." Very little was known about the properties and behavior of steam, and the interrelation of heat, work, and energy was not even dreamed of. Caloric theory was in the ascendancy. This was the scientific state of affairs in the years when Watt made his great contributions to the development of the heat engine. What, then, were these basic inventions, how did Watt arrive at them, and what were his training and educational background?

James Watt (1736–1819) came from a family of teachers, mathematicians, instrument makers, and contractors. He had a thorough classical education and excelled at geometry. At seventeen he was sent to Glasgow to work as an apprentice at mathematical instrument making. This highly technical vocation furnished another term for identifying the "engineer" of that time. When Watt was twenty-one, he attempted to open up his own shop but was blocked by the corporation of Hammermen on the ground that he had not served his proper period of apprenticeship. However, a family friend came to Watt's rescue and got him an appointment as mathematical instrument maker for Glasgow University. This was a fortunate break for young Watt; it provided an atmosphere where his natural mathematical and scientific talents could flourish. He quickly made friends with Dr. Joseph Black, who was then deep in his experimental study of heat, and with other professors of natural philosophy, or physical science as we now call it. The faculty at the university respected him and treated him as an equal. In fact, he was destined to establish himself firmly in later years as a "man of science," in addition to his reputation as an engineer. His interest in science extended to chemistry, and he became an intimate friend of Joseph Priestley. He was credited with the discovery of the composition of water prior to Henry Cavendish's discovery of it. Watt studied both German and Italian in order to read original technical papers in theoretical mechanics and other sciences from those countries. When he was forty-eight years old, he became a fellow of the Royal Society of Edinburgh, and a year later received the same honor from the Royal Society of London. In 1806 he received the LL.D. degree from the University of Glasgow and everywhere was recognized as both an eminent scientist and engineer.

This, then, was the type of man who was asked to investigate the trouble in the Newcomen engine at Glasgow University in 1764. The engine had previously been shipped to London for an investigation and modification by factory experts, but the results were not satisfactory. After considerable study Watt concluded that the trouble was in the boiler. The only way that boilers could be designed in those days was through the use of empirical equations and tables; that is, design based on experience rather than theory. On the basis of the empirical design procedure, the boiler appeared large enough, but Watt determined that it was actually too small to balance the load placed on the engine for the particular application in which it was used. His success in resolving this problem gave Watt an incentive to concentrate further on the general problem of steam engine economy and efficiency.

As the Newcomen engines were made in larger and larger sizes, the thin brass cylinders were replaced with thicker and heavier cast-iron cylinders. The sheer mass of metal required more and more steam during the upward stroke of the piston because more heat was now required to bring the cylinder up to steam temperature. Conversely, more cooling water was required also to cool the cylinder while condensing the steam during the downward power stroke of the piston. Watt recognized this conflict but needed experimental information on specific heats[2] of materials and properties of steam, particularly latent heats of vaporization and condensation.[3] Since little reliable information was available, he proceeded to determine these physical constants himself, within the limitation of the experimental equipment available to him. Then on the basis of these unsophisticated data, he calculated that the amount of steam required to operate a steam engine was the amount necessary to fill the cylinder, plus the additional amount necessary to heat the cooled cylinder walls, the piston, the accumulated water

[2] The amount of heat required to raise one pound of the material one degree in temperature.

[3] The amount of heat required to boil water into steam, or the amount of heat that must be removed to condense steam into water.

left in the cylinder, and the sealing water on top of the piston, all these to be heated to the temperature of the incoming steam by means of the latent heat of condensation. To this amount, he calculated, must also be added the steam used in expelling water and air out through the "snifting valve" (see Fig. 6) during the upstroke of the piston.

Watt's calculations indicated that only one-third of the total steam consumed in the Newcomen engine was being used for the purpose intended—to fill the cylinder and produce a vacuum. He concluded that the balance could be saved through proper engine design. The solution was obvious once he had isolated and recognized the problem. He used a *separate vessel* to condense the steam during the downstroke of the piston; a valved pipe connected the vessel to the steam cylinder. In this system he could keep the cylinder and piston at the entering steam temperature at all times and thus greatly reduce the amount of cooling water required since now the only heat removed was the latent heat of condensation from the exhausting steam. But some provision had to be made to remove the condensed steam, the injected cooling water, and air that accumulated in the condenser under vacuum conditions. These he removed with a reciprocating vacuum pump that had been developed years before. He also suspected that there might be an advantage in introducing the steam to the top rather than the bottom of the piston, and thus pushing down with steam during the power stroke rather than using atmospheric pressure. He was able to accomplish this by inventing a "stuffing box" (Fig. 7) that sealed the steam in the top of the cylinder while permitting the piston rod to move in and out with the piston. This invention left only one further difficulty to be overcome. How could the piston be returned to the top of its stroke with a vacuum underneath it? Watt solved this problem by con-

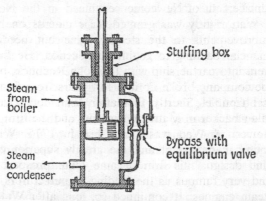

Fig. 7. Cylinder containing a stuffing box and equilibrium valve

necting the upper and lower ends of the cylinder with a pipe and "equilibrium valve," which could be opened at the proper instant to break the vacuum by allowing the steam above the piston to move below the piston. The counterweight on the walking beam then could pull the piston to the top of its stroke and complete the cycle.

To the casual observer, Watt's early engines and the Newcomen engine were similar in general appearance. The walking beam principle was retained, and the reciprocating motion was used primarily for pump applications. The differences were fundamental, however, and operating experience proved that Watt's original calculations on estimated steam consumption were astonishingly accurate. In fact, many of Watt's engines were sold on a contract that called for periodic payment of one-third of the fuel saving from the replacement of Newcomen engines.

Watt rightly was granted basic patents on his improvements to the steam engine but needed financial backing to go into production. He first went into partnership with Dr. John Roebuck, but the company broke up in a few years from financial trouble. Shortly thereafter Watt found another backer in Matthew Boulton, and the firm of Boulton & Watt was established in 1775. With sound management and the greatly superior engine design, this firm became quite prosperous and very famous as the leading manufacturers of steam engines. It continued so, long after Watt's death.

Watt, of course, continued with the experimentation on and development of his steam engine. Boulton encouraged this as he was interested in the widest possible application and maximum sales of the firm's product. It became increasingly apparent that there was a very real need for an engine capable of producing rotative power directly. The old scheme of using a steam engine to pump water to an overhead reservoir to operate a water wheel was too cumbersome and inefficient.

It was on Boulton's insistence that Watt began studying this problem, and came to the conclusion that a crank mechanism offered the most promise. He was preparing to patent this device when one of his workmen, James Pickard, revealed the secret to a competitor. Pickard and the competitor obtained the patent together and then offered it back to Watt for a price.

This brazen dodge so infuriated Watt that he refused to have anything further to do with the crank mechanism. Instead, he attempted to develop other designs for producing rotary motion and finally came up with his sun and planet wheel mechanism. This apparatus consisted of two meshing gears, one fastened rigidly to the rotating shaft and the other fastened to the rod connected to the walking beam, as shown in Fig. 8. This was a planetary gear train and had a theoretical advantage in that the number of revolutions of the shaft per cycle of engine operation could be varied by changing the relative diameters of the meshing gears. However, the gear design and manufacturing techniques in use at that time were quite primitive. Gears were cast with no machined surfaces whatsoever. Because of the excessive gear friction, the engines built to this design were noisy and inefficient.

Watt's unfortunate experience with the crank mechanism probably delayed the effective use of the steam engine for rotary motion for some time, although there is evidence that he finally did employ the crank to some extent before Pickard's patent expired. The whole episode is a strange

Fig. 8. Sun and planet gear on Watt engine

one since the basic crank mechanism was shown in writings of at least 200 years earlier. (See Fig. 4.) Watt probably could have used it with impunity notwithstanding Pickard's patent, and it is puzzling that the patent was issued in the first place.

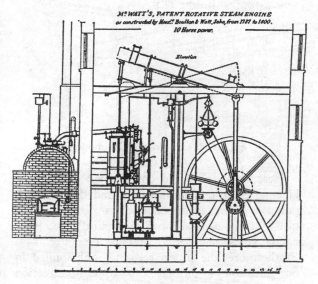

Fig. 9. Double-acting Watt engine

By 1782 Watt had patented a double-acting engine, Fig. 9. In this design he introduced steam from the boiler to *each* end of the cylinder, alternately. Thus he got two power strokes per cycle rather than the one obtained previously. At the end of each power stroke the steam was exhausted through suitable valves to a vacuum condenser.

This arrangement eliminated the need of a counterweight on the walking beam and increased the power of the engine for a given size, but it presented a new complication. He could no longer use the chain-and-sector type of walking beam (see Fig. 6), because now the piston pushed as well as pulled during each cycle.

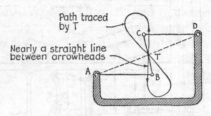

Fig. 10. Watt's straight line motion

Here was a new and complicated problem in kinematics. The steam cylinder and the vacuum-pump cylinder each contained a piston with a piston rod that must move in a parallel, reciprocating (back and forth) manner (see Fig. 11). Furthermore, the piston rods not only *pulled* in one direction but *pushed* in the opposite direction as well. This complication required a rigid linkage of intricate design that had never been used. Watt solved this problem in characteristic fashion by inventing his straight-line motion mechanism (Fig. 10) and combining it with the pantograph parallel mechanism as shown in Fig. 11.

Watt's straight-line mechanism was not mathematically perfect, but a sufficiently close approximation, and in fact is the most widely used straight-line mechanism in machine design today. This mechanism can be seen in both Figs. 10 and 11 as the linkage *A-B-C-D,* with the point *T* moving in a straight line. *A* is a fixed point on the frame of the engine, *D* is the center of the walking beam, and *H* is the journal bearing for the rotating shaft, all three points fixed to the engine frame. The pantograph parallel motion mechanism is seen in Fig. 11 as the linkage *D-E-F-B-C,* with the point *F* moving parallel to point *T* and therefore also in a straight line. As we have said, Watt's earlier engines used a planetary gear train instead of the crank *G-H* as shown.

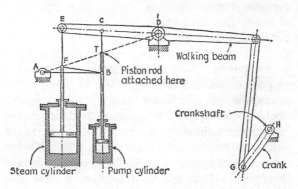

Fig. 11. Beam engine with straight-line and parallel motions

Watt patented this mechanism in 1784, and it continued in use, with modifications, for many years until machine tool techniques had advanced to the point where long true flat surfaces could be machined. The true surfaces were then used to guide crossheads,[4] thus permitting the abandonment of the cumbersome walking beams and the development of more compact engines.

The historical development of the heat engine seems to have followed a typical pattern. First there was a basic idea in the mind of the inventor that either showed promise of some fundamental improvement over its predecessor or operated on an entirely new concept. This idea was followed by the construction of a prototype model and then a rapid commercial exploitation in an ever-expanding industrial economy. Next there was a period of improvement and refinement in which the heat engine type was brought to a high state of perfection. This engine then remained supreme until another engineering or scientific breakthrough occurred and a new heat engine was born with significantly higher efficiencies, lower weight to power ratios, greater mobility, or some other advantage in which the existing heat engines could not compete. This pattern of development has existed right up to the present day, but as we shall see in the following pages, the different fundamental types of major engineering breakthroughs in heat engine development have not been many.

It is important that we recognize that these fundamental discoveries have come from great crea-

[4] A crosshead is a block moving along a smooth straight bearing surface as a guide, and serving as a connection between the piston and connecting rod. Its action can be seen clearly in Fig. 13, as the mechanism through which the reciprocating piston drives the wheels of the locomotive.

tive minds, well educated in the basic sciences and engineering sciences extant in their day. We should also recognize the important part that patent laws have played in heat engine development. Patents have been not only a powerful incentive to creative and inventive engineers and scientists but also an important factor in attracting financial backing by giving reasonable protection to expensive and risky manufacturing projects.

Watt continued to make minor improvements on his engine. He developed the poppet valve, which opened and closed automatically against a restraining spring pressure and which is widely used in compressors today. He also invented a steam-pressure gauge and an engine indicator[5] which would trace on an indicator card the pressure-volume history of the steam in the cylinder throughout its cycle. The indicator has been used ever since on all types of reciprocating engines and compressors to permit study of the performance of the equipment. Watt also developed a throttle valve and the flyball governor (see Fig. 9) as a servo-operated, or self-acting, constant speed control device. Watt did not invent the flyball governor, as the principle had been in use for a number of years in flour mills to control the distance between millstones. He did, however, perfect its application to steam engines so that constant predetermined speeds could be automatically maintained.

[5] The engine indicator is described in detail on page 122 and illustrated in Fig. 20.

In 1800, Watt's basic patents expired, but by that time the Boulton & Watt firm had produced over 500 engines, of which 38 per cent were pumping engines and the balance used for supplying rotative power to such industry as textile mills, rolling mills, and flour mills. The industrial application and marketing of the steam engine brought out the need for some standard method of rating. Some unit of power was needed so that one engine could be compared with another, proper selling prices established, and correct application made to balance engine with load. It was perfectly natural that the term "horsepower" should have been used quite early to compare the power of the steam engine to the horse-operated machinery it displaced. Savery used the term first when he devised a system for rating his fire engines. His engine horsepower rating was determined on the basis of the horses it displaced directly, plus those maintained in pasture between the shifts necessary to keep an equivalent horse-operated pump running twenty-four hours a day. He justified this rating on the argument that all his fire engines could operate twenty-four hours a day without rest. However, he said nothing about the size or strength of the horses he referred to, and the term was, of course, very unreliable.

John Smeaton continued to use the term but fixed the work of one horsepower as equivalent to the work a horse would do in lifting 22,916 pounds a height of one foot against the force of gravity. Still other horsepower values appeared, and for many years the horsepower unit had in fact little meaning.

Watt was determined to put an end to this confusion. He performed a series of experiments to establish a value for the horsepower unit that would be acceptable to everybody. He determined that the average horse could raise 1 cwt[6] to a height of 196 feet in one minute, and could continue working at this steady rate until replaced by a relief horse. He than increased this figure by 50 per cent, to ensure that the purchasers of his engine would have no complaint, and arrived at a figure that is equivalent to 33,000 ft-lbs per minute. This figure finally prevailed, probably due to Watt's prestige, and is the definition of the horsepower unit today.

Watt's patent of 1782 stated that he proposed to use the expansive force of steam by letting it continue to expand and do work after its admission to the cylinder had been cut off. Now this was a very important discovery that struck at the heart of a loss that years later in thermodynamics would be called "irreversibility." This is the loss that occurs when the steam remaining in the cylinder under pressure at the end of the power stroke is allowed to discharge by throttling either to the condenser or to the atmosphere without doing any work in the process of discharge. A knowledge of thermodynamics is necessary to understand the real significance of this phenomenon. (We shall discuss it later.)

[6] 1 cwt = 112 lbs.

Although Watt was on the right track, he did not appreciate the importance of his proposal, for he failed to exploit it in any of his engines. In order for him to effectively use the expansive force of steam, it would have been necessary to go to much higher boiler pressures than the 4 to 6 pounds per square inch that he usually employed. This he consistently refused to do. After all, his heat engine was the greatest thing the world had ever seen, it worked fine—and, besides, high-pressure boilers would be dangerous to life and property. Perhaps Watt was somewhat content to rest on his laurels, and on the comfort and prestige of his established position. If so, other impatient, younger engineers were not convinced. Let us see who they were and what they did.

The Steam Engine After Watt

In the generation that followed James Watt, three men stand out as having made significant contributions to the development of the steam engine. One was an American, Oliver Evans (1755–1819), and the other two were Englishmen, Jonathan Hornblower (1753–1815), and Richard Trevithick (1771–1833).

Evans's contributions were probably the most remarkable when we consider the great handicaps under which he worked. He was born on a farm in Delaware and attended country school until he was fourteen. He then apprenticed himself to a wagonmaker, where his mechanical ingenuity immediately became apparent. Significantly though, he was not content to develop only his mechanical skill, but was determined to get a scientific education on his own. Wherever he could find them he sought out books on technical and theoretical subjects, particularly mathematics and mechanics, and mastered them during his free hours. When he was seventeen, he had an opportunity to study Watt's new steam engine design with its separate condenser. Watt's design made such a profound impression that Evans devoted the rest of his life to the development of the steam engine and its utilization.

It is always interesting to know just how an inspirational thought or creative idea comes to a man. One day Evans was idly observing some boys playing around the neighboring blacksmith's fire. They had got an old gun barrel from somewhere and filled it with water, rammed the muzzle tight with a wad, and placed the breech in the fire. The resulting crack sounded like a gunpowder explosion and dramatically impressed Evans with the great energy in expanding steam. This incident convinced him that Watt was not properly utilizing this energy in his low-pressure engines, and so he began to experiment with high-pressure steam and its "elastic power."

The obstacles confronting Evans, however, were nearly insurmountable. He was a poor man of humble origin and surroundings. Because he was self-educated, he had no scientific status or prestige, and so his ideas faced constant public ridicule. Nevertheless, his ideas were sound, and with great perseverance he obtained limited financial backing and moved ahead. In 1786 he was ready to make his move, and he petitioned the legislatures of Pennsylvania and Maryland for exclusive rights to use his improvements in steam engines and steam carriages in those states. Pennsylvania refused that part of the petition concerning steam carriages on the grounds that the idea was so ridiculous that they could not waste their time giving it serious consideration. Evans had reasoned correctly (although there was no theoretical basis with which to prove it) that the high-pressure steam engine, using the "elastic power" of the steam after its admission into the cylinder had been cut off, would raise the power and efficiency of the steam engine to the point where it could be utilized in small sizes to propel land vehicles. However, the accident of his humble birth and education, plus the fact that he lived in a new frontier country with little technology, effectively blocked his dream of a steam carriage. Thirty-three years later, George Stephenson designed the *Rocket,* the first successful steam locomotive, which ran on rails between Liverpool and Manchester, in England. There is little doubt that with proper encouragement and financial support, Evans could have done the job earlier in America.

As it was, Evans concentrated on promoting stationary engines, and by 1802, in the city of Philadelphia, he produced his first small, high-pressure steam engine (Fig. 12) with a 6-inch bore and 18-inch stroke. The venture cost him

$3700; at the age of forty-seven, he spent his entire resources on it.

Evans's engine proved to be of a remarkably sound design. It developed rotative power through a crankshaft and flywheel operating at thirty revolutions per minute. Evans modified the walking beam and positioned its fulcrum at the end of a rocking link. With these changes he was able to translate the straight-line motion of the piston rod to the rotary motion of the shaft in a simpler design than the Watt straight-line mechanism. The beam had a peculiar loping motion when operating, and it became known as the grasshopper type.

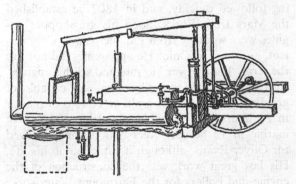

Fig. 12. Evans's steam engine

The boiler was also a sound improvement. It was a horizontal copper cylinder with the flue running through the center before connecting with the chimney. Since the hot flue gases passed through the boiler tube as well as around the outside of the boiler, the heat transfer surface was increased. The basic design is quite similar to the Scotch marine-type boilers used today. With the engine operating at high pressure, Evans could eliminate the condenser and simply exhaust the steam to the atmosphere after it had expanded in the cylinder. This simplified the design and initial cost, but at a price. Evans did not realize that in abandoning the condenser he lost most of the efficiency he had gained from the higher boiler pressures. Engineers were to discover later that the best arrangement was to use *both* Evans's high pressure boiler and Watt's vacuum condenser.

Evans could now demonstrate, beyond all doubt, the soundness of his ideas. Financial backing followed quickly, and in 1807 he established the Mars Iron Works. Soon his grasshopper engines were working from Philadelphia to Connecticut, and west to Ohio. He apparently did not use the term "horsepower" to rate and sell his engines. Instead, he would describe them as "capable of grinding 300 bushels of grain or 12 tons of plaster in 24 hours," or "capable of cutting 100 feet of marble in 12 hours." Recognition finally arrived for Oliver Evans, although it came late in his life. His last great work was the construction of the engine and boilers for the Fairmount Waterworks in Philadelphia. This engine had a 20-inch bore and 5-foot stroke and operated with four boilers at 200 pounds per square inch pressure.

Jonathan Hornblower was born in England, just two years before Evans and seventeen years after Watt. A member of a family of distinguished engineers, he had a better formal education than

Evans, and, being English, he became one of Watt's strongest competitors, although he seemed always to be overshadowed by Watt's greater reputation and prestige. Nevertheless, Hornblower did make one basic contribution to steam-engine design in his compound steam engine. In this design he admitted steam to an initial cylinder, similar to Watt's system, but then, instead of throttling this steam to the condenser after the power stroke, he passed it to a second lower pressure cylinder, where it did additional expansive work before going to the condenser. Here again was a fundamental improvement that the inventor could not adequately understand or explain on a scientific and rational basis, simply because the engineering science on which it was based had not yet been worked out. Hornblower could not exploit his design adequately because the pressures he used were too low to take advantage of compound expansion. Furthermore, he did not have accurate steam properties or thermodynamic relationships that would have enabled him to design the correct relative sizes of the two cylinders. Later on, his associate Arthur Woolf did manage to work out a design that was more successful, and because of its higher efficiency it eventually became quite popular in France in those areas where fuel was expensive.

The compound engine was destined to become a very important type of design in later years, but Watt would not concede at the time that the idea was new and basic, and alleged infringement on his patents. A long and involved lawsuit followed, finally to be won by the Boulton & Watt firm in 1799. Hornblower lost the case primarily because he could not convince the court of the theoretical advantages that were present; unfortunately, he did not adequately understand them himself. The long legal battle broke Hornblower financially, and he never recovered. In different circumstances his creative mind may have gained more recognition. At the age of fifty-two, ten years before his death, he wrote some technical descriptions of a "new steam wheel" that looked similar to the steam turbine that was to come later, but he never got around to exploiting his idea.

Richard Trevithick's major contribution to steam-engine development paralleled that of Evans; namely, the exploitation of high-pressure steam.

Sixteen years younger, Trevithick, an Englishman, had many advantages that Evans never had. His father was the general manager of the Dolcoath coal mine, where a Newcomen engine was installed when Richard was still in knee pants. He grew up in an atmosphere of engineering, technology, and industry, and had a good education based on science and mathematics. He received his engineering training by serving an apprenticeship with both Hornblower and William Murdock, one of Watt's assistants. It was a rather common practice among the English firms to train young engineers at the factory by having them first help with the construction of a steam engine and then go with the engine to install it and place it in operation for the new owners. We must remember that manufacturing techniques in 1800 were much different from today's. Piece parts and assemblies were handmade to fit one particular machine. There was little control of limits and tolerances and no interchangeability of parts. Gears, cylinders, etc., were roughcast and hand-fitted by chipping and filing. It took considerable art to assemble such a machine and get it to run at all. Points of excessive binding and friction had to be relieved, and adjustments and modifications had to be made. This usually took a long time and the engineer frequently stayed with the engine as a permanent job.

It was in such an environment that Trevithick's inventive abilities flourished. He concluded, independent of Evans, that there would be some fundamental advantages to utilizing steam at high pressure, and about 1800, on a highly ingenious design, he built a double-acting, high-pressure engine with a crank, for mine operation. As Evans did, he discarded the condenser as now unnecessary, and thus unknowingly lost much of the economy he had gained in going to high pressure. His engine exhausted steam to the atmosphere at somewhat elevated pressures and was quite noisy compared to Watt's condensing engines. It came to be known as a "puffer," to distinguish it from the Boulton & Watt-type engines.

It was inevitable that accidents would happen with the development of high-pressure boilers. It happened to one of Trevithick's early engines when the operator tied down the safety valve to get more power from the engine. Watt had invented the mercury manometer for measuring the low pressures in his boilers, but high-pressure steam gauges were not developed until about 1848. The only way of knowing what pressures were being developed in high-pressure boilers was to "pop" safety valves, set at some known pressure. These safety valves were merely known weights, placed on discs covering boiler openings of known area; at the designed pressure the weights lifted and allowed the steam to escape. Little was known regarding the theory of strength of materials, and progress in high-pressure boiler design came only through painful trial-and-error procedure, sometimes with disastrous results.

Trevithick worked on improved safety controls, and one of his most effective and foolproof devices was a fusible plug of lead, placed in the boiler shell below the normal water line. As long as the plug was covered with water it remained intact, but when the water level became too low the plug was exposed and melted, and the flashing, hissing steam warned the operator. Excessive pressure also blew out the plug if the safety valve did not function.

Adapting the Steam Engine to Transportation

In this same period, the early part of the 19th century, the first successful attempts were made to adapt the steam engine to transportation vehicles. This introduced many problems of adaptation, both to the engine and to the vehicle that was intended to carry it. The weight and vibration of the engine had to be reduced, a fuel supply had to be carried, and enough space left over to carry a pay load. There were new perplexing problems of control and safety, and mechanisms had to be designed to propel the vehicle effectively.

The steamboat came first. Man's attempt to free himself from the undependable power of sails goes back to the slave galleys of the ancients. Fanciful paintings and drawings of paddle-wheel boats propelled by man power or animal power were shown as early as the 14th century. A steamboat design was first patented by Jonathan Hulls in 1737, after Newcomen's engine had become established. It was a stern paddle-wheel design in which ratchets were intended to supply rotary motion. Fortunately, no attempt was made to build it; it could never have worked. The proposed drive mechanism was too fanciful and the Newcomen engine was simply too heavy and inefficient.

As the steam engine developed, however, there were more and more persistent attempts to find some way to apply this new source of power to ship propulsion. Strangely enough, the main impetus in this development came from America. The great seafaring nation of England was indifferent to it all, probably due to the excessive conservatism of the British Admiralty. By 1787 John Fitch had a paddle-wheel steamboat operating on the Delaware River. It attracted enough attention that the framers of the Constitution, who were gathering in Philadelphia at the time, went down to see it. Fitch's steamboat was abandoned the following year, however, because of its inability to carry an adequate pay load. The first commercially successful steamboat was the *Clermont,* built by Robert Fulton, and placed in operation on the Hudson River in August 1807. Fulton made no contribution to the development of the steam engine. The engine he used was a standard model, purchased from Boulton & Watt. His achievement was in being the first to integrate a hull and power plant in an economical design. The steamboat developed rapidly after the *Clermont,* and was soon used extensively on inland waterways. In 1819 the steamship *Savannah,* also American, made the first transatlantic voyage with the help of auxiliary sail power. England soon got the point and started steamship development with a vengeance. The first Cunard liner, the *Britannia,* began transatlantic service in 1840. She displaced 1154 tons and was driven by a single-cylinder engine supplied from four boilers operating at 9 pounds per square inch pressure. The engine developed 740 horsepower and drove the ship at a speed of 8½ knots.

Around 1800 it looked as if the first successful commercial development of steam-powered land transportation would be in the form of steam carriages operating on ordinary roads. Indeed, the earliest attempts were in this direction. A French military engineer, Nicholas Cugnot, was the first to build a full-sized, steam-driven road vehicle, in 1769. It was clumsy, top-heavy, and so underpowered that it could hardly move. It was a mere curiosity that impressed no one, particularly the Field Artillery officers for whom it was intended.

Both Oliver Evans and Richard Trevithick gave serious engineering study to this problem, and Trevithick had some success in making a prototype model in 1801, but he lacked perseverance in this field and directed his energies toward locomotives on rails. Here he had more success. By 1804 he had a small steam locomotive operating on trial runs on a Welsh coal road. His engine hauled five trailing cars at a speed of 5 miles per hour. He used a horizontal cylindrical boiler, similar to Evans's, with the return flue passing through the boiler. He devised the scheme of exhausting the steam from the cylinder into the smokestack through a jet to increase draft, and was the first to couple four wheels together to make them all driving wheels. But his locomotive had many problems that needed further development. For instance, if the single-cylinder engine happened to stop on dead center, there was no way of getting it started again unless everybody got out and gave the locomotive a push. Trevithick never completed the necessary development work, and when the engine jumped the track one day, he gave up in disgust and set it up to do stationary engine work.

The man credited with being the inventor and founder of the railways was George Stephenson (1781–1848), born in Newcastle, the son of a colliery fireman. By the time he was seventeen he had become a "plugman," the man in charge of a coal pit pumping engine. Stephenson had unusual mechanical ingenuity but was entirely self-educated. He developed great skill in repairing Watt engines, and was appointed engine-wright in 1812. With this background he was well qualified to pursue his interest in a "traveling engine." He made no basic contribution to steam engine development, but, like Fulton with the steamboat, he was the first to co-ordinate a rail carriage and power plant into an economically successful design.

Stephenson received financial backing from the colliery owners where he worked, and began the tedious but necessary experimentation and improvisation of his traveling engine. He used two cylinders and placed the cranks 90 degrees apart so the engine could never stall on dead center. His engine was successful, and in 1814 it drew a load of thirty tons up a 1 in 450 incline at four miles per hour. Stephenson continued to develop the steam locomotive with dedication and perseverance. When the Liverpool and Manchester Railway Company decided to offer a prize of 500 pounds in a public competition for the best locomotive that could meet certain stipulated conditions, Stephenson was ready. At the historic event, held near Liverpool in October 1829, Stephenson's *Rocket* (Fig. 13) won on all counts. It ran 12 miles in 53 minutes and met all other stipulated conditions.

This event established beyond doubt that the heat engine would permanently displace the horse as the prime mover for hauling heavy loads over long distances.

Up to this time scientists and engineers had given no serious thought to developing a flying

Fig. 13. Stephenson's Rocket

machine powered by a heat engine. A few men
were beginning to make free balloon flights, using
the newly discovered hydrogen gas, but the weight
factor was so critical that all thought of powered
flight had to wait until there were many more
breakthroughs in heat engine development and in
the engineering science of thermodynamics upon
which it is based.

CHAPTER 3

ORIGINS OF THERMODYNAMICS

From 1702, when Savery first began the commercial manufacture of his fire engine, until 1829, when George Stephenson demonstrated his locomotive at the historic Liverpool competition, engineers had developed the heat engine with very little theoretical understanding of the fundamental processes involved.

It is true that the technical knowledge necessary for the intelligent design of machine *mechanisms* was now available. Mathematics had become quite sophisticated. Analytical geometry had been invented in the early 17th century, and the calculus was in a continuing state of development. Mechanics had emerged as an engineering science defined as "the science of motion, of its cause and its effects; also the science of machines." Newton's laws of motion were firmly established, and the concepts of force, mass, acceleration, and universal gravitation were understood by scientifically educated men. In fact, the entire subject of mechanics had been organized into a useful body of knowledge in Newton's great work, *Principia,* published in 1687. In this same year Pierre Varignon (1654–1722) prepared a manuscript (published after his death) entitled *Project d'une Nouvelle Méchanique,* which was unique in that it was a treatment of mechanics organized in the form of a textbook with the subject matter arranged in the following order:

1. Axioms, hypotheses or postulates, and propositions
2. Weights supported by cords
3. Pulleys
4. Wheel and axle
5. Levers
6. Inclined plane
7. Screw
8. Wedge
9. General principles of the simple machine
10. Equilibrium of fluids

Thus we see that at least a rudimentary knowledge of mechanics and mechanisms was available in published form as early as Savery's time, and this knowledge was doubtlessly used by the earliest steam engine builders in designing the levers, wheels, shafts, and other components of their machines.

But notwithstanding the steady progress of mathematics and mechanics, it is quite remarkable that so little was known about the measurable properties of matter, the laws governing the behavior of fluids and solids, and the nature of energy, particularly the interrelationships of different forms of energy. It seems almost incomprehensible to us now that scientific knowledge could advance through Galileo, Descartes, and Sir Isaac

Newton without a clear understanding of the principle of the conservation of energy, and that until the middle of the 19th century most of the world's respected physicists should still be convinced that heat was a material substance that somehow could be squeezed in and out of matter.

Carnot's Contributions to Thermodynamic Theory

The great scientific breakthrough in the development of heat engine theory came in 1824 in most unlikely circumstances. It was the publication of a memoir[1] entitled "Reflections on the Motive Power of Heat" by an obscure young French physicist and artilleryman, Sadi Carnot (1796–1832). This paper created no excitement at the time and lay virtually unnoticed for twenty-five years. Yet today it ranks with the greatest of the scientific classics, and has made Carnot immortal in the field of physical science.

We may well wonder why the scientific world did not recognize this great contribution earlier. There are several reasons. Carnot was an unknown physicist whose career was a curious mixture of academic, military, and industrial experience. He wrote his monumental paper when only twenty-three years old and died tragically, only eight years after it was published and before he had time to exploit his great theories. Also, communication and the dissemination of scientific lit-

[1] Technical paper, in today's language.

erature were poor in those days. Only a small number of copies was printed, and most of them were lost. In fact, there was difficulty finding an original copy when a second edition was published in 1872. Then, too, no one expected in those days that any significant contribution to heat engine theory would come from Paris, France. England was the seat of steam engine development, and had been for a hundred years.

And so it was that twenty-five years elapsed until the eminent English physicist Lord Kelvin rediscovered Carnot, and together with the German physicist Rudolf Clausius wrote the definitive memoirs that established the classical thermodynamics. With this new science, engineers were quickly able to bring the heat engine to the higher plateaus of development as we know it today, and the end is not yet in sight. Thus, we must first become acquainted with Carnot, and with his classic principle, before we can really appreciate the story of heat engines.

Nicolas Léonard Sadi Carnot was born on June 1, 1796, in Paris. He was a frail, sensitive child, who showed an early talent for mechanics, physics, and mathematics. His father, the noted French general Lazare Nicolas Marguerite Carnot, gave scientific direction to Sadi's education. During this period French educational institutions were in a turmoil. The French Revolution had just been concluded, and the Napoleonic wars had begun. The technical schools that had supplied civil and military engineers to the state were disorganized, and so the Ecole Polytechnique was established. Its mission was to train engineers for both public and private service, and it quickly became one of the foremost schools of the day. It had on its staff such men as Lagrange and Laplace in mathematics, Prony in mechanics, and other eminent scientists. It maintained its standards by limitation of enrollment and highly competitive entrance examinations.

Carnot prepared for this school and was admitted in 1812 at the age of sixteen; his advancement was rapid and his record distinguished. After graduation he attempted to enter the field artillery school at Metz. His interest in a military career was understandable in view of the political upheavals of that period. He was too young, however, and had to continue his studies in Paris for a while. Later he had an "in-and-out" military career, but he always took advantage of any opportunity to further his education. He attended courses at The College of France, the Sorbonne, the Ecole des Mines, and the Bibliothèque. He also had some limited experience with industry, and it was there that he first became acquainted with the steam engine and sensed its great industrial and economic potential.

Carnot was struck by the lack of theory and the total reliance on empirical procedures by which steam engines were designed. With rare perception he concluded that,

if the art of producing motive power from heat were to be elevated to the stature of a science, the whole phenomena must be studied from the most general point of view, without reference to any particular engine, machine, or operating fluid.

To elevate the art to a science became the dominating goal of the last thirteen years of his short life. He wrote his great paper in 1819, but it was not accepted for publication until 1824. Throughout this period he performed research on gases and vapors and pursued scientific studies with great energy. His scientific stature was recognized by his contemporaries, and he became a member of the Association Polytechnique. Unfortunately, Carnot's paper was written (for reasons discussed later) on the premise that the caloric theory was valid. Actually, from his unpublished notes one is safe in concluding that he had serious doubts of the validity of this theory and was ready to throw in his lot with the small group of physicists who stubbornly insisted that heat was some form of motion or dynamics in matter. Evidence was gradually accumulating that heat and work were somehow related, and Carnot planned a series of experiments to see whether the expenditure of work and the appearance of heat always existed in a fixed relationship. Had he been able to proceed with this work, he might have thrown a much earlier light on the equivalence of heat and work and the conservation of energy. As it was, the Revolution of 1830 interrupted his research, and he returned to military service. Upon release from active duty he plunged back into his scientific studies with such an intense effort that it apparently affected his frail health. He wrote friends that he had "inflammation of the lungs" followed by scarlet fever. Then, while he was recuperating from this serious illness, an epidemic of cholera went through his town. He succumbed on August 24, 1832, at the age of thirty-six.

Carnot started his epic memoir with the following introduction, in which he states his objective. Note that his prediction of the future of the heat engine was prophetic.

The fact that heat can produce motion is obvious to everyone. The steam engine is well known. It also causes agitation of the atmosphere, ascension of clouds, fall of rain, meteors, currents of water, volcanic eruption, etc. Nature has provided us with combustibles on all sides and thus has given us the power to produce at all times and places, heat and the impelling power which is the result of it. The study of heat engines is of the greatest interest, their importance is enormous, and they seem destined to produce a great revolution in the civilized world. Already the steam engine works our mines, impells our ships, excavates our ports and rivers, forges iron, fashions wood, grinds grain, spins and weaves cloth, transports the heaviest burdens.

If some day the steam engine shall be so perfected that it can be set up and supplied with fuel at small cost, it will combine all desirable qualities, and will afford to the industrial arts a range, the extent of which can scarcely be predicted. It is not merely that a powerful and convenient motor that can be procured and carried anywhere, is substituted for the motors already in use, but that it causes rapid extension in the arts in which it is applied, and can even create entirely new arts.

The most signal service that the steam engine has rendered to England is undoubtedly the revival of the working of the coal mines, which had declined and threatened to cease entirely, because of the difficulties of drainage and raising the coal. It may be said that coal mining has increased 10 fold in England since the invention of the steam engine. It is almost equally true in regard to the mining of copper, tin and iron in mines in England and the new world. It has permitted the establishment of regular communications across the seas, etc., etc.

The discovery of the steam-engine owed its birth, like most human inventions, to rude attempts which have been attributed to different persons, while the real author is not certainly known. The important discovery is not the first attempt but the successive improvements. There is almost as great a distance between the first apparatus in which the expansive force of steam was employed and an existing machine (1824), as between a raft and modern vessel. The honor of this early development belongs to England. Savery, Newcomen, Smeaton, Watt, Woolf, Trevithick & others.

Notwithstanding the work on all kinds of steam engines, their theory is very little understood, and attempts to improve them are still directed almost by chance.

The question has often been raised whether the motive power of heat is unbounded, whether the possible improvements in steam engines have an assignable limit,—a limit which the nature of things will not allow to be passed by any means whatever, or whether on the contrary, these improvements may be carried on indefinitely. We have long sought to ascertain whether there are in existence agents preferable to the vapor of water for developing the motive power of heat; whether atmospheric air, for example, would not be preferable. We propose to submit these questions to a deliberate examination.

Carnot first deduced that if one was to study the mechanical effect or work that can be produced by heat, a fluid must be allowed both to receive and to reject heat during a series of processes culminating in a *cycle* of operation. He noted that in a cycle the fluid would always return exactly to its original state or condition. Thus he correctly reasoned that any work done or heat rejected during a cycle must all come from the original quantity of heat supplied, and would be independent of the particular fluid that happened to be used in the cycle. This fact must be true since the fluid, in periodically returning to its original state, must periodically cancel out whatever effects it might have had in absorbing heat or producing work in the cycle. He then examined the steam engine and noted that it operated in the following cycle. Heat was transferred to water in the boiler as the water evaporated into steam, the steam in expanding did work, the steam next was condensed into water when heat was removed from it in the condenser, and finally the water was pumped under pressure back into the boiler and thus returned to its exact original condition. Now what, he asked, was the net result of this cycle of operations? Some heat was absorbed from the furnace at a high temperature, some mechanical effect was produced as work done by the engine, some heat was transferred out of the condenser at low temperature, and a small amount of work was used by the pump in pumping the water back into the boiler. Since the small amount of work necessary to drive the pump could come from the work produced by the engine, the actual net effect was this: work was produced entirely by "letting down" heat from a high temperature source to a low temperature receiver.

Carnot noted the fundamental point that in any cycle he could conceive there would always be these elements: heat added, work done, heat rejected. He summed it up in one sentence: "The thermal agency by which mechanical effect may be obtained is the transference of heat from one body to another at a lower temperature." Note carefully that although Carnot's first example was based on the steam engine, his conclusion was general and would apply to any working substance, gas or vapor. (See Fig. 14.)

Carnot next considered the problem of determining the maximum work that could be realized from the transfer of heat from high to low temperature. By remarkable reasoning he deduced a definition of a *perfect thermodynamic engine,* in his own words, "Whatever amount of mechanical effect it can derive from a certain thermal agency, if an equal amount be spent in working it backwards, an equal reverse thermal effect will be produced." Such an engine has come to be called a *reversible engine* and the quotation is the celebrated Carnot Principle.

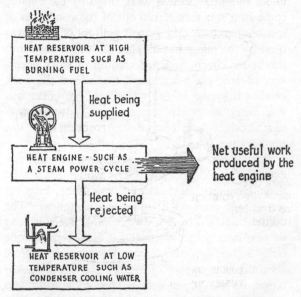

Fig. 14. Basic flow diagram for a heat engine

Let us see if we can explain this in another way. The Carnot Principle says in effect that the maximum amount of work that can be produced by any heat engine operating between a given high temperature source and low temperature receiver is the work produced by a reversible engine operating between those same temperature limits. The key word here is "reversible," and the significance of this concept of reversibility will be explored in considerable detail in Chapter 4. It might be well, however, to take a little time here to see how a reversible process can be used as an indicator of maximum output.

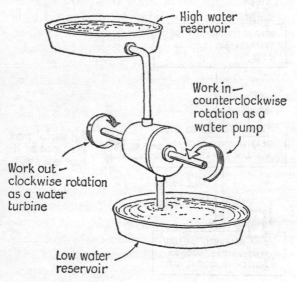

Fig. 15. Reversible water turbine

Imagine a water turbine, Fig. 15, that produces work from the energy of water's falling from a high reservoir to a low reservoir. This is analogous to heat's "falling" from a high temperature reservoir to a low temperature reservoir. If all the potential energy in the water is converted to work at the turbine *without friction loss,* then this *same amount of work* could be used to run the turbine backward, as a turbine pump, and pump all the water back into the high reservoir. But if the turbine had any bearing friction or fluid turbulence present in its operation, this drain would reduce the amount of useful work available at the shaft; this reduced amount of work would no longer be sufficient to pump the water back up to the high reservoir when the turbine was reversed. In other words, the maximum turbine output would occur when the entire process and energy output could be *exactly* reversed. Thus the test of reversibility is a criterion of a "perfect" water turbine.

Unfortunately, Carnot's original proof was fallacious, because his original premise was based on the caloric theory of heat. On this theory the same amount of heat would be rejected from the condenser that was supplied by the boiler, and under these conditions, Carnot showed no engine could be more efficient than a reversible engine without creating a perpetual motion machine.[2] Fortunately, Carnot's Principle, though based on a false premise, was still true, and both Kelvin and Clausius later placed it on a sound, rigorous, thermodynamic basis by establishing a new concept, the Second Law of Thermodynamics (about which you will hear later). The only cloud on Carnot's memoir was his acceptance of this caloric theory

---

[2] Carnot reasoned that if a more efficient engine did exist, it could be used to run a reversible engine backward, thus pumping all the caloric leaving the condenser back to the boiler, but still having some power left over to do useful work. The two engines operating together would then constitute a heat engine system, operating continuously with no net loss of energy.

of heat. Actually, he accepted it not through any conviction of his own, but rather in deference to the best scientific opinion of his day. It is true that Count Rumford, in his cannon-boring experiment, and Humphry Davy, in his ice-friction experiment, both performed about twenty-five years earlier, had demonstrated that heat could not be a material substance. But these experiments lacked precision and were intended more to show what heat was not, rather than what it was. An hypothesis as firmly rooted as the caloric theory could not easily be overturned, and it remained the "correct" view of physicists and chemists for many years after Carnot's death.

For his concept of how work is produced from heat, and in further analysis of his reversible cycle, Carnot correctly concluded that the efficiency of any heat engine must depend on the *temperature* at which the heat is both received in the boiler from the source and rejected to some receiver such as the cooling water of the condenser (see Fig. 14). He stated the following as principles that should not be disregarded:

1. The temperature of the fluid should be made as high as possible in order to obtain a large production of motive power [heat supplied at the highest possible temperature].
2. For the same reason the cooling should be carried as far as possible [heat rejected at the lowest possible temperature].
3. It should be so arranged that the passage of the elastic fluid from the highest to the lowest tem-

perature should be due to increase in volume and should occur spontaneously as the effect of rarefaction [in other words, a reversible adiabatic expansion, which we shall explain later].

Carnot stated that the maximum limits of temperature between which any actual heat engine can work are simply the temperature of combustion and the temperature of the coldest body we can easily find and use in nature, usually the water of the locality. Carnot realized the great difficulties of taking advantage of the highest temperature ranges. High temperatures in steam involve very high pressures, and low temperatures result from the expansion of the steam to enormous volumes, both conditions difficult to fulfill in engine design. He sensed that here was the real challenge in the design of the steam engine.

Carnot stated clearly that the advantage of high-pressure steam engines was fundamentally in the greater *temperature* drop utilized; but to utilize this advantage to the maximum the steam must be expanded to the lowest possible *pressure*. In other words, he eloquently showed the fundamental advantage of using the condenser of Watt, a device that was later abandoned by Evans and Trevithick in their high-pressure engines because it was considered unnecessary. Carnot's insight also explained the advantage of Hornblower's compound expansion engine.

Carnot went on to discuss the advantages and disadvantages of using permanent gases (air) as the working medium.

1. It would cool more rapidly by an equal increase in volume [referring to the advantage of a maximum temperature spread in the cycle].

2. Vapors can be formed only through the intervention of a boiler, while atmospheric air could be heated directly by combustion carried on within its own mass. [Here he clearly anticipated the automobile engine and other internal combustion engines.]

3. In order to give air great increase in volume, and by that expansion a great change in temperature, it must first be taken under sufficient *pressure*, by a pump or other means, before heating it. This operation would require a special apparatus not found in steam engines. [All internal combustion engines today employ a compression process prior to ignition.]

4. The condensing of the vapor by contact with the refrigerant body is much more prompt and easier than cooling air. There might, of course, be the expedient of throwing the latter out into the atmosphere, which would also have the advantage of avoiding the use of a refrigerant. [Here he again anticipated modern internal combustion engine design.]

5. One of the gravest problems with steam engines is the high boiler pressure. There is no such problem with heating air. We might conceive even the possibility of making the same heat act successively upon air and vapor of water. It would be necessary only that the air should have after its use an elevated temperature, and instead of throwing it out immediately to the atmosphere, to make it envelope a steam boiler, as if it issued directly from a furnace. [This is

the same basic idea that now is being tried by incorporating a gas turbine ahead of a conventional steam power cycle.]

Carnot understood the limitations of steam and water but expressed the following doubt of ever finding a better substitute. "If we could find an abundant liquid that would vaporize at a higher temperature than water and with a smaller specific heat, which would not attack the metals employed in the construction of the machine, it would undoubtedly merit a preference. But nature provides no such body."

Carnot discussed a proposal that was made at that time to use alcohol instead of steam in power cycles. He pointed out that a machine had been built for the express purpose of using it, on the theory that it would produce more work since alcohol possessed a "stronger tension" (higher pressure) than water at the same temperature. Carnot maintained that these people were going off in a blind direction and would only multiply the problems that resulted from higher boiler pressures. He summarized his reaction to the proposal as follows: "As to the relative advantage in a greater production of motive power—an advantage attributed to it—we know by the principles above demonstrated that it is imaginary." Here was Carnot's firm recognition that *temperature* and not *pressure* was the fundamental criterion in determining heat engine efficiency. We shall see in later chapters just why this is true.

With his concept of a perfect thermodynamic

engine, Carnot could now compare actual steam engine performance with the performance theoretically possible in a reversible heat engine operating between the same temperature limits. He concluded his paper with just such an analysis, using performance data from existing steam engines. No attempt will be made here to follow the mathematics and thermodynamics of Carnot's solution, which, from the state of the science at that time, was quite cumbersome. His reasoning can best be followed after an elementary foundation of thermodynamics is established in the succeeding chapters. Suffice it to say that his solution of the work done by a theoretically perfect heat engine involved, first, the formulation of a hypothetical *reversible* steam engine cycle. Then, by analyzing the processes in the cycle, and using higher mathematics and certain thermodynamic relationships, he was able to calculate the maximum "mechanical effect" the heat engine could produce.

He then compared this with existing steam engines. Here are his own words:

The engines which up to this time have shown the best results are the large double-cylinder engines used in the drainage of the tin and copper mines of Cornwall. The best results that have been obtained from them are as follows: 65 millions of pounds of water have been raised one English foot by the bushel of coal burned (the bushel weighing 88 pounds). This is equivalent to raising, by a kilogram of coal, 195 cubic metres of water to a height of one metre, producing thereby 195 units of motive power per kilogram of coal burned.

195 units are only the twentieth of 3920,[3] the theoretical maximum; consequently only $\frac{1}{20}$th of the motive power of the combustible has been utilized. Most engines are greatly inferior to the example given. The old engine at Chaillot [probably a Newcomen engine], for example, raised 20 cubic metres of water 33 metres for 30 kilograms of coal consumed, or 22 units of motive power per kilogram—180 times less than the maximum possible.

The numerical accuracy of Carnot's analysis was not important. What was tremendously important, however, was that he had supplied engineers with a method to compare actual heat engines with a maximum theoretical performance.

The essence of Carnot's contribution can be briefly stated as follows:

1. Establishing the concept of the heat engine as a continuously operating cycle in which work is produced by receiving and rejecting heat.
2. Establishing the concept of the perfection of the reversible cycle.
3. Realization that the fundamental criterion of efficiency is the difference of temperatures between which the heat engine receives and rejects heat.

For reasons previously discussed, Carnot's memoir remained buried for many years. A few

[3] Carnot had previously *estimated* by a rather devious and incomplete mathematical treatment that one kilogram of carbon, producing 7000 units of heat in burning, could theoretically produce 3920 units of motive power in "falling" from 1000°C. to 0°C.

physicists from time to time sensed its fundamental greatness but could do nothing with it. Some rejected it entirely because it was based on the caloric theory of heat. On the other hand, others were so impressed by Carnot's brilliant reasoning that they were blinded into using his paper as their justification for retaining the caloric theory. Heat engine theory—and, in a larger sense, thermodynamics—was stalled on dead center until the great enigma of heat, work, and energy could be resolved. Up to this time, energy was a concept related to the motions and positions of bodies. Out of the earlier work of Newton, Huygens, Leibniz, and others, came the concepts of force, mass, acceleration, momentum, work, and both potential and kinetic energy. The principle of conservation of *mechanical* energy was recognized, but heat was something else again. The thought that there might be some *general* principle of conservation of energy that also would encompass heat was daring and radical, but the seeds were being planted and the ideas were germinating.

Heat: a Form of Energy

Since the experiments of Count Rumford and Davy, a small but growing body of scientists had become converted to the dynamical theory of heat. But it was not until 1842 that any quantitative experimental results were published showing the mechanical equivalence of heat. In that year Dr. J. R. Mayer of Heilbrom, Germany, published a paper in which he postulated the general equivalence and conservation of all forms of energy. He calculated that the "warming of a given weight of water from 0° Centigrade to 1° Centigrade corresponds to the fall of an equal weight of water from a height of 365 metres." He arrived at this result by assuming a process in which all the work done in the compression of air appears as heat, and then calculating the mechanical equivalent of heat from the ratio of specific heats of air at constant pressure and constant volume.

Although the priority and significance of Mayer's work are now generally recognized, his paper received little attention at the time of publication. He had no academic position or prestige, and his views were heretical to the established position. Later events showed that the scientific elite would not be convinced until they had comprehensive and massive evidence from one of their own members. This evidence came shortly from James Prescott Joule (1818–1889).

Joule was born in Salford, England, and reared in nearby Manchester. He came from a prosperous family and received a good education. He became a methodical experimental physicist renowned for precision measurements and fine experimental technique. Having grown up in the industrial center of the world, Joule associated with engineers, and his career was influenced by their technical problems.

The physicist's concept of energy was a mathematical function, one half the mass of a moving object multiplied by the square of its velocity.

Newtonian mechanics recognized that "work" was the product of force and distance, but this concept was entirely different from the "work" term used by engineers in designating the effect of mechanical action in overcoming resistance. Engineers used the term "accumulated work" for designating what we now call internal energy, and they considered any work spent in overcoming friction as "annihilated power." Joule, in his associations with these different people, recognized these anomalies, and became convinced early that heat and work were manifestations of the same thing. He threw his prestige and reputation as an experimental physicist behind the mechanical theory of heat, and started a long series of experiments to determine the most exact value possible for the mechanical equivalent of heat. His experiments took many different forms. One of the more famous was in the use of falling weights to turn paddle wheels, which churned water. The rise in the water temperature indicated the amount of heat converted from the work of the moving weights.

Joule first described his research at a meeting of the British Association in 1843 and then again in 1845. Although he did not arouse much excitement, he continued his methodical experimentation. Then, at a scientific meeting at Oxford on June 27, 1847, he again was scheduled to present a paper on his latest results. Present at this meeting was a brilliant young physicist by the name of William Thomson. Although only twenty-three, Thomson already had published twenty-six papers on mathematical physics and was creating quite a stir in the scientific world.

Thomson had come to this meeting for the express purpose of criticizing Joule's work. Why? A short time earlier he had studied a copy of Carnot's memoir and was profoundly impressed by the original creative reasoning he found there. It blinded him into an acceptance of the caloric theory that had formed the basis of Carnot's paper. Notwithstanding this bias, Thomson listened attentively to what Joule had to say, and before the end of the presentation, he became convinced that he was hearing some fundamental truths. As a result, he did not get up to criticize, but introduced himself to Joule privately at the end of the meeting. There he struck up a lifelong friendship, in which Joule was often to act as a catalyst to Thomson's brilliant mind. The great paradox of heat and work was not immediately resolved after the Joule-Thomson meeting. Although Thomson was greatly impressed by Joule's apparently unassailable demonstration of the conversion of work into heat, he still could not reject Carnot's theory. As we shall see, the answer finally came to him in 1850, just three years later.

William Thomson[4] (1824–1907) was born in Belfast in the year Carnot's memoir was published in Paris. He skipped the usual formalities of schooling, but was educated by his father, who was Professor of Mathematics at the University of Glasgow. Thomson matriculated there at the ten-

---

[4] Knighted as Lord Kelvin in 1866 at the age of forty-two.

der age of ten, and published twelve research papers before he was graduated. He was appointed Professor of Natural Philosophy (physics) in 1846, when only twenty-two, the year before he met Joule. Thomson established an early interest in the theory of heat as a result of some associations he had with Henri Victor Regnault, a French chemist, at the time when the latter was determining some constants of heat and steam for use in steam engine development. Later study of Carnot's great work greatly stimulated Thomson's interest, and his subsequent association with Joule finally convinced him that here was a fundamental area of science that needed development. He attacked this field with great vigor and in 1849 published a very important and scholarly paper entitled, "Carnot's Theory of the Motive Power of Heat with Numerical Results Deduced from Regnault's Experiments on Steam." It was as a result of this paper that Carnot literally was rediscovered and reintroduced to the scientific world. Thomson's star already had risen high. He spoke with prestige and authority, and the scientific world listened to his words.

The following quotation, taken directly from Thomson's paper, best states its objective:

> The sole effect to be contemplated in investigating the motive power of heat is resistance overcome, or, as it is frequently called, work performed, or mechanical effect. The questions to be resolved by a complete theory of the subject are the following.

1. What is the precise nature of the thermal agency by means of which mechanical effect is produced, without effects of any other kind?

2. How may the amount of this thermal agency necessary for performing a given quantity of work be estimated?

In the following paper I shall commence by giving a short abstract of the reasoning by which Carnot is led to an answer to the first of these questions; I shall then explain the investigation by which, in accordance with this theory, the experimental elements necessary for answering the second question are indicated; and, in conclusion, I shall state the data supplied by Regnault's recent observations on steam, and apply them to obtain, as approximately as the present state of experimental science enables us to do, a complete solution of the question—the nature of thermal agency, considered as a motive power.

Thomson concluded his paper with an analysis of the performance of actual steam engines. The following quotation is illuminating in that it uses the language of engineers of the day to describe a practical engineering problem—this, in a technical paper prepared by one of the pre-eminent theoretical physicists of the world. Here was evidence not only of an influence of engineering on physics but, more important, of an influence of physics on engineering, an influence that has been growing stronger and stronger to the present day.

To obtain some notion of the economy which has actually been obtained, we may take the alleged performances of the best Cornish engines, and some other interesting practical cases, as examples. From this point of view, we see very clearly how imperfect is the steam engine, even after all Watt's improvements. For to push the principle of expansion to the utmost, we must allow the steam, before leaving the cylinder, to expand until its pressure is the same as that of the vapor in the condenser. According to "Watt's law," its temperature would then be the same as (actually a little above, as Regnault has shown) that of the condenser, and hence the steam-engine worked in this most advantageous way has in reality the very fault that Watt found in Newcomen's engine.[5] This defect is partially remedied by Hornblower's system of using a separate expansion cylinder, an arrangement the advantages of which did not escape Carnot's notice, although they have not been recognized extensively among practical engineers, until the last few years.

1. The engine of the Fowey Consols mine was reported, in 1845, to have given 125,089,000 foot-pounds of effect, for the consumption of one bushel or 94 lbs. of coal. Now the average amount evaporated from Cornish boilers, by one pound of coal, is 8½ lbs. of steam; and hence for each pound of steam evaporated 156,556 foot-pounds of work are produced.

The pressure of the saturated steam in the boiler may be taken as 3½ atmospheres; and, consequently, the temperature of the water will be 140° (Centigrade). Now the latent heat of a pound of

---

[5] Thomson is here referring to the waste of heat due to the initial condensation of steam when admitted to a cold cylinder.

saturated steam at 140° is 508, and since, to compensate for each pound of steam removed from the boiler in the working of the engine, a pound of water, at the temperature of the condenser, which may be estimated at 30°, is introduced from the hotwell; it follows that 618 units of heat are introduced to the boiler for each pound of water evaporated. But the work produced, for each pound of water evaporated, was found to be 156,556 foot-pounds. Hence 156556/618, or 253 foot-pounds, is the amount of work produced for each unit of heat transmitted through the Fowey Consols engine. Now in Table II,[6] we find 583.0 as the theoretical effect due to a unit descending from 140° to 0°, and 143 as the effect due to a unit descending from 30° to 0°. The difference of these numbers, or 440, is the number of foot-pounds of work that a perfect engine with its boiler at 140° and its condenser at 30° would produce for each unit of heat transmitted. Hence the Fowey Consols engine, during the experiments reported on, performed $253/440$ of its theoretical duty,[7] or 57½ per cent.

In other words, Thomson was able to determine through theoretical computations that one of the most efficient steam engines of the day was producing power at only a little more than half of its theoretical capabilities. Unfortunately, Thomson's paper of 1849 still used the caloric theory of heat as its basis. Up to this time he had been unable to

[6] In this Table Thomson had calculated the theoretical work possible for a reversible heat engine operating between various temperature limits.

[7] Foot-pounds of work done per pound of coal burned.

reconcile Carnot's work with Joule's convincing research. However, he continued to ponder the problem and finally, about a year later, succeeded in resolving this great dilemma. Before he could publish his discovery, the solution suddenly appeared from an unexpected quarter. It was in a classic paper entitled, "On the Moving Force of Heat and the Laws of Heat which may be Deduced Therefrom," written by Rudolf Clausius (1822–1888), and published in a German journal, *Paggendorff's Annalen,* in May 1850.

Clausius was a most highly regarded mathematical physicist, and a contemporary of Thomson, being only two years younger. He was born in Köslin, Pomerania, a province of Germany. He was a brilliant student during his schooling at the gymnasium at Stettin, and also during his four years (1840–1844) at the University of Berlin. He took his degree in 1848 and was appointed Professor of Physics in the Royal Artillery and Engineering School at Berlin in 1850, the year he wrote his first famous paper on thermodynamics.

Clausius's paper was both incisive and comprehensive. He gave Thomson credit for clarifying and interpreting the theories of Carnot and the researches of Joule, and bringing out the difficulties of the contradictions in them. He wrote,

> Nevertheless we ought not to suffer ourselves to be daunted by these difficulties, but, on the contrary, we must look steadfastly into this theory which calls heat a motion, as in this way alone can we arrive at the means of establishing it or

refuting it. Besides this, I do not imagine that the difficulties are so great as Thomson considers them to be, for although a certain alteration in our way of regarding the subject is necessary, still I find that this is in no case contradicted by proved facts. It is not even requisite to cast the theory of Carnot overboard, a thing difficult to be resolved upon inasmuch as experience to a certain extent has shown a surprising coincidence therewith. On a nearer view of the case, we find that the new theory is opposed not to the real fundamental principle of Carnot, but to the addition "no heat is lost," for it is quite possible that in the production of work, both may take place at the same time; a certain portion of heat may be consumed and a further portion transmitted from a warm body to a cold one, and both portions may stand in a certain definite relation to the quantity of work produced. This will be made plainer as we proceed, and it will be moreover shown that the inferences to be drawn from both assumptions may not only exist together, but that they mutually support each other.

The First and Second Laws of Thermodynamics

You will recall that Carnot, following the caloric theory, had assumed that the quantity of heat rejected from the engine was the same as that supplied to it (see Fig. 14). Even though this assumption was false, he was able to prove his proposition that a reversible engine was a "perfect" engine by showing that any alternative would result in a perpetual motion machine. Clausius now showed that of the heat supplied to the heat engine a portion is *converted* into mechanical effect or work and the remaining portion rejected from the engine to the lower temperature receiver. However, he was able to retain the fundamental truth of Carnot's principle regarding the reversibility of a perfect engine, by showing that any alternative would violate the following axiom:

It is impossible for a self-acting machine, unaided by any external agency, to convey heat from one body to another at a higher temperature.

This proposition has come to be known as the Clausius statement of the Second Law of Thermodynamics. The proof of Carnot's principle based on this statement of the Second Law is given in the appendix.

Clausius went on to do monumental work in the years 1850–1865 in developing the classical thermodynamics. During that period he published nine scholarly memoirs that advanced thermodynamics rapidly as a highly mathematical and theoretical science. He consolidated these memoirs into a book, published in 1865, which was the first systematic treatment of thermodynamics as a separate discipline. In his fourth memoir of the series, Clausius discovered the existence of an abstract thermodynamic property that he later called entropy. This function has proven to be one of the most powerful tools in the thermodynamic analysis and development of heat engines. (We shall see how it is used in Chapter 6.)

Thomson did not have an opportunity to read Clausius's memoir of 1850 until a year after it was published. In the meantime he came independently to the same conclusion on how to reconcile the great truths of Carnot and the dynamical theory of heat. He published his new views in the *Transactions of the Royal Society of Edinburgh,* March 1851, in a paper entitled, "On the Dynamical Theory of Heat, with Numerical Results Deduced from Mr. Joule's Equivalent of a Thermal Unit, and M. Regnault's Observations on Steam." In this paper he gave proper credit to Clausius, but claimed independent discovery of the Second Law of Thermodynamics, stating the following axiom, which is of vital importance to our purpose here:

It is impossible, by means of inanimate material agency, to derive mechanical effect from any portion of matter by cooling it below the temperature of the coldest of the surrounding objects.

The axiom given above by Thomson has come to be known as the Kelvin statement of the Second Law of Thermodynamics. Through thermodynamic reasoning it can be shown to be equivalent to the Clausius statement of the Second Law.

Thomson stated in his paper that the whole theory of the motive power of heat is founded on two propositions. The first proposition (now called the First Law of Thermodynamics) was stated in his words as follows: *"When equal quantities of mechanical effect are produced by any means whatever from purely thermal sources, or lost in purely thermal effects, equal quantities of heat are put out of existence or are generated.*" The second proposition he referred to was based on his statement of the Second Law. Clausius also recognized that thermodynamics was primarily based on these two hypotheses, and so it has evolved down to the present time.

With the powerful support of both Thomson and Clausius, the dynamical theory of heat was now established, and the caloric theory was dead and buried, once and for all. The Principle of the Conservation of Energy, of which the First Law of Thermodynamics is a more limited statement, was not the result of one man's work or discovery. Its history is complicated, and often confusing and contradictory. It has even been proposed that there is a sociological explanation of its discovery, that the Industrial Revolution brought on an economic structure that could not be operated without an exact knowledge of the equivalence of different forms of energy. It was necessary to put a price on power—water power, engine power, man power, and fuels such as coal and oil—to make these items barterable. Therefore this led to the unconscious discovery of *energy,* the common denominator, and its convertibility to various forms. Be that as it may, the Principle of the Conservation of Energy is a very broad concept that extends beyond thermodynamics into other disciplines. It forms the basis of the First Law of Thermodynamics only insofar as it applies to finite systems, such as heat engines, in which heat and work are mutually convertible forms of energy.

Thermodynamics now rapidly developed as a new body of knowledge. Its origin was due to the intellectual achievements of the three creative geniuses, Carnot, Thomson (Lord Kelvin), and Clausius. Others contributed much, of course. Early contributors such as Boyle, Hooke, and Davy; contemporaries of Thomson and Clausius, such as Joule, Rankine, and Clapeyron; and later contributors such as Gibbs and Planck, all were invaluable in the parts they played. Thermodynamics soon became a universal requirement in the curricula of engineering colleges and universities. Textbooks on the subject began to appear, and engineers received not only the basis for understanding the broad principles on which heat engine theory is based, but powerful mathematical tools as well, whereby they could design new types of heat engines and bring them all to higher levels of perfection.

To understand the development of modern heat engines then, we must have some understanding of what thermodynamics is. This subject is, of course, highly technical, usually given at the junior level in engineering curricula. But, in the following section, we shall try to reach a sufficient understanding of the subject to increase our appreciation of the modern heat engines of today.

CHAPTER 4

THERMODYNAMIC PROPERTIES AND PROCESSES

Basic Concepts

By the latter half of the 19th century, physicists and engineers in the field of heat engine theory no longer had to waste their efforts wading through a morass of false and contradictory hypotheses. The First and Second Laws of Thermodynamics now became unassailable precepts around which a new science grew. It was this science of thermodynamics that provided the theory by which existing heat engines could be analyzed and improved, and entirely new heat engine concepts created and their performance predicted, prior to the construction of expensive prototype models. We might say that thermodynamics originally evolved directly out of the heat engine concept, and was the method by which physicists described this important physical phenomenon in fundamental terms. Thus the heat engine cannot be understood without some knowledge of thermodynamics, anymore than an electric motor can be understood without some knowledge of electricity and magnetism. And the degree to which we understand an engine or motor depends on the degree or depth to which we can comprehend the particular science on which it is based.

Thermodynamics has developed into a broad and comprehensive science with many ramifications far beyond heat engine theory. However, it is not within the scope or intent of this book to treat the philosophical aspects of this subject or to delve into its extensive mathematical expressions. Nevertheless, we believe that it is possible to investigate thermodynamics, to the extent that it can illuminate our general understanding of heat engine principles as enunciated by Carnot and his later colleagues, without the competence in higher mathematics and physics that would be required for a detailed mastery of the subject. We believe that it is possible, within these limitations, to appreciate fully the significance of the heat engine cycle, the Second Law of Thermodynamics, the Carnot Principle, the concepts of entropy and reversibility, of efficiency as a function of temperature, and of the universality of these things to all heat engines, past, present, or future, whether idealized conceptions or actual operating machines, regardless of their size, shape, design, type of fuel used, or type of fluid passing through the machine.

To begin, let us consider some aspects of two heat engines with which we are all familiar, the steam engine and the automobile engine. Obviously, both engines consume heat to produce work, and so are called heat engines. The steam engine burns fuel *externally* to produce steam in a boiler.

The fuel is usually one of the so-called fossil fuels —coal, oil, or gas, but other heat sources could be used, nuclear fuels in an atomic reactor or the sun's energy in a solar furnace. On the other hand, the automobile engine burns its fuel *internally,* using gasoline or some other liquified petroleum product. The engine is so designed, of course, but beyond that the automobile is a mobile heat engine and must carry its fuel along with it in a convenient form.

We also observe that both types of heat engines continuously pass fluids through them and operate in a cyclic manner. The steam engine circulates steam from a boiler through the prime mover, then through a condenser, where the steam is condensed into water, and finally through a boiler feed pump, where it is pumped back into the boiler, thus completing a *closed* cycle. If the condenser is omitted, the engine can still operate on an *open* cycle by simply blowing the exhaust steam to the atmosphere. But if we look at the latter arrangement closely, we see that we still have a cycle of operation, since every pound of water supplied to the boiler must be replaced with a pound of the exhaust steam which in time will condense out of the atmosphere. In other words, nature herself eventually closes this open cycle.

You will recall that the early steam engine builders were divided in their opinions whether a steam engine condenser was necessary or even advantageous. Watt originally used the condenser to good advantage. Evans and others later abandoned it because they thought it unnecessary with their high-pressure engines. But none of these men understood the real significance of the condenser. Thermodynamics gives us the answer, as we shall see.

Like the steam engine, the automobile engine passes a fluid through itself in a cyclic operation, but in an entirely different way. A mixture of air and gasoline vapor is first drawn into the cylinders during a suction stroke, next it is compressed and ignited after a compression stroke, then the hot gaseous products of combustion are expanded during a power stroke, and finally these products are ejected from the exhaust pipe in the exhaust stroke, thus completing an open cycle.[1] We find this feature of *cyclic operation* in all heat engines that are capable of continuous action. Carnot was the first to recognize the significance and used it in establishing his criteria of perfection.

Considering some further common aspects of the performance of the steam engine and automobile engine, we notice that both reject heat. The cooling water necessary to operate a condenser, the hot steam exhausted from a non-condensing steam engine, and the hot exhaust gases ejected from an automobile exhaust pipe are all evidence of this rejection. We may wonder about this. Isn't energy being wasted since the heat was generated in the first place so that it could be converted into work? Would it not be better to design an automobile engine that had a cold exhaust and

[1] Because of the nature of its design and operation, the automobile engine is called a reciprocating internal combustion engine.

could thus convert all the generated heat energy into horsepower? Such an engine might give us three times more miles per gallon than we now get. Thermodynamics shows us that this is an impossibility, *even in theory,* and, what is more important, it tells us precisely how much heat *any heat engine* can convert into work, and how much must irretrievably be lost regardless of our refinements of design or our search for new inventions.

It would help us to answer these questions, and many others, if we could design an imaginary heat engine in its simplest form, stripped of all auxiliary components such as valves, gears, flywheels, power take-off shafts, etc. At the same time we should want it to be able to receive heat into a fluid system, operate continuously in a cyclic manner, produce work, and eliminate that quantity of heat that cannot be converted into work. In other words, our simplified engine should have those essential features that are common to all heat engines.

Such a heat engine is shown in Fig. 16. It is simply an insulated cylinder containing some fluid such as steam, water, or air, and a frictionless and weightless piston holding some weights. We can see that if we placed this apparatus on a high-temperature heat reservoir, heat would flow into the cylinder, expand the fluid, and do work by raising the weights. Next we could cause the piston to return to its initial position if we put the cylinder in contact with a low-temperature reservoir, thus causing heat to flow out of the system and contract the fluid. In this manner, then, by alternately using high- and low-temperature heat reservoirs, and by adding weights to the cylinder at a low elevation and removing weights at some higher elevation, we would have a continuously acting heat engine in the form desired. It is true that this apparatus does not *look* like any engine you may be familiar with, and furthermore there

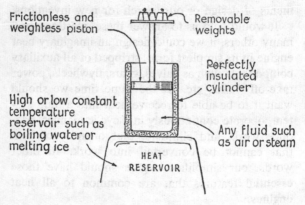

Frictionless and weightless piston

Removable weights

Perfectly insulated cylinder

High or low constant temperature reservoir such as boiling water or melting ice

Any fluid such as air or steam

HEAT RESERVOIR

Fig. 16. Basic heat engine

is little prospect that an actual heat engine built and operated in this manner would have any practical value. But that, of course, is not its purpose. The value and uniqueness of this imaginary apparatus are that there are only two external effects: (1) the heat added to or removed from the system at the respective heat reservoir temperatures, and (2) the useful work either done by or performed on the system due to the rising or falling weights. In other words, if we call the fluid contents of the cylinder a thermodynamic *system* and the containing walls of the cylinder and piston its *boundaries,* we can simplify the description of this heat engine by saying it is a system across whose boundaries flow only heat (at the reservoir temperatures) and work. The simplicity holds because the piston is frictionless, the cylinder is perfectly insulated, and the working fluid remains contained in the cylinder at all times. With this apparatus we can now examine the different processes and cycles by which heat and work can be converted into other energy forms, free of the influence of any other extraneous effects or complicating factors.

Work, Heat, and Energy

If we want to discuss and understand heat engines in the language of thermodynamics, we must use its terminology with precision. We have been using the terms energy, heat, and work, on the assumption that these are common terms familiar to everyone. Let us now examine the thermodynamic definitions of these terms and see how they compare with your present understanding of them.

Work is defined as a force moving through a distance. A piston lifting weights is doing work, just as a turning wheel does work in moving your automobile. The units of work are usually expressed in foot-pounds (ft-lb). One ft-lb is equal to a force of one pound moving a distance of one foot. *Heat* is energy that is transferred between two regions because of a difference in their temperatures. We receive heat *radiation* from the sun because its surface is about 10,800°F. hotter than the surface of the earth. We can boil coffee because the high temperature burner on the stove *conducts* heat through the coffee pot, and we can heat our home with a furnace because the hot surfaces of the furnace are at a higher temperature than the room air circulating through it, and thus heat it by *convection*. Although the mechanism by which the heat is transferred happens to be different in each of the three examples just given, this fact need be of no concern to us here. The significant thing to remember is that wherever there is a temperature difference heat will flow, regardless of what particular substance may be in the intervening space, or whether in fact there is any substance there at all. Insulating materials can slow down the transfer of heat, but they can never stop it. In engineering terminology heat is ordinarily expressed in units of Btu (British Thermal Units). One Btu is the amount of heat required to raise the temperature of one pound of water one degree Fahrenheit.[2]

Energy is a fundamental concept of thermodynamics and difficult to define in a satisfactory manner. This should not astonish us; as we have seen, it took the physicists until the middle of the 19th century to come to a clear understanding of

---

[2] Since the specific heat of water (the amount of heat required to raise the temperature of one pound one degree) varies very slightly with temperature and pressure, the Btu is defined precisely as the amount of heat required to raise the temperature of one pound of water from 59.5°F. to 60.5°F. at standard atmospheric pressure.

the nature of energy. Perhaps for our purpose we can best think of energy as *something* that can be manifested in different ways, and of which work and heat are two different forms, each of which we have defined. There are other forms in which energy can exist, as we shall see presently.

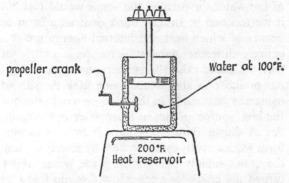

Fig. 17. Cylinder and piston apparatus

With these descriptions in mind let us now perform some simple experiments with our cylinder and piston apparatus as shown in Fig. 17, and get a clearer understanding of the convertibility of energy into different forms. First, suppose we place one pound of water in the cylinder at 100°F. and place it on a heat source at 200°F. Heat will now flow into the cylinder continually until the temperature of the water rises to 200°F. We can quickly calculate the amount of heat transferred as 100 Btu. But what has happened to this heat? It has been *stored* in the water in the cylinder, except for the very small amount that has left the system in the form of work. (The weights would be lifted very slightly due to the expansion of the water.) This stored heat is now called *internal energy*. We must be careful here not to think of this internal energy as only some different form of heat just because heat was used to raise the temperature of the water, or because the water would feel hot if we touched it. Instead think of it as a form of *energy* of which heat and internal energy are two entirely different manifestations. As a matter of fact, we could raise the temperature of our original pound of water to the same 200°F. without using any heat at all. In this case we would remove the heat source and insert a propeller in the cylinder as shown. This would now permit us to perform work directly on the system by simply turning the crank rapidly and churning the water. If we turned the crank long enough, we would find that the water would steadily rise in temperature until it again reached the 200°F. But what has now happened to the *work* put into the system? According to the First Law of Thermodynamics, as stated by Kelvin and others, this work energy cannot be destroyed and so must be accounted for. It is accounted for as 100 Btu of internal energy. And if we next place the cylinder in contact with a 100°F. heat reservoir, we would find that the 100 Btu of energy would now leave the system as heat, as the temperature of the water gradually dropped back to the original 100°F.

During the crank-turning process just described no heat transfer occurred at all. This type of process is of particular interest in thermodynamics and is given a special name. Any process that occurs without heat's being transferred across the boundaries of the system is called an *adiabatic process*. We will be using this term again.

The ease with which an experimental apparatus could be set up, using a propeller or paddle wheel to churn water, suggests that it could be used to determine the mechanical equivalent of heat. We recall that it was Joule, the friend and colleague of Lord Kelvin, who did precisely this. Although this experiment looks deceptively simple, it actually requires the highest degree of experimental skill to get accurate energy measurements and a truly adiabatic process. Joule had the reputation of being a precise experimental physicist, and he performed this experiment many times, over many months, and with different types of liquids. His final conclusion was that it took 772 ft-lbs of work to raise the temperature of one pound of water one degree Fahrenheit. The most recent work in determining the mechanical equivalent of the Btu has been done by the National Bureau of Standards, U.S.A., and they place the value at 778.2 ft-lbs per Btu. To avoid the confusion caused by constantly changing and refining the value of this constant, the First International Steam Table Conference in 1929 in effect defined an *International Btu* as being equal to 778.26 ft-lbs. They fixed the magnitude of Btu in terms of a previously defined unit and thus avoided the necessity of further calorimetric measurements.

Returning again to our piston and cylinder apparatus, we can perform another interesting experiment in which both heat and internal energy can be transformed directly into work. This time we put a quantity of air in the cylinder at a temperature of, say, 100°F.; we next place two 5-pound weights on the piston and then isolate the cylinder from any heat source so that any process that may occur must be adiabatic. The piston with the weights on it will now come to equilibrium with the air pressure in the cylinder, but if we suddenly remove one of the weights, the piston will rise until the air expands to the new equilibrium pressure. If the piston rises one foot, the system produces 5 ft-lbs of work. Where does this work come from? It does not come from heat because we made the process adiabatic. The answer, of course, is that it must come from the *internal energy* of the air.

One of the thermodynamic facts about a gas such as air is that the amount of internal energy it contains is a function only of its temperature.[3] Joule first discovered this in another one of his classic experiments, and it has come to be known as Joule's Law. In other words, regardless of what kind of process you perform on a gas, if its temperature rises or falls, its internal energy accordingly goes up or down, and if there is no change in temperature, there can be no change in internal energy. Accordingly, in the foregoing experiment the drop in internal energy could have been verified by noting a corresponding drop in the tem-

[3] Rigorously true only for *perfect* gases, but very nearly true for actual gases such as air.

perature of the air. You have observed the same phenomenon, no doubt, if you have changed a tire on your car. The valve stem on a tire gets cold when you suddenly remove the valve core to deflate the tire; conversely, you feel the tire hand pump get hot when you pump up a tire.

But how about converting heat directly into work? Is it possible to do this in a single process? To answer these questions let us place our cylinder containing 100°F. air on a heat reservoir also at 100°F. On the piston platform we place a large number of very small weights and allow the system to come to equilibrium. We now remove the weights, one at a time, and accordingly the piston will slowly rise as the system attempts to remain in equilibrium. But as each small weight is removed, the temperature of the air in the cylinder drops slightly, and so some heat immediately flows into it from the reservoir and thus keeps it at 100°F. At the end of this process a certain amount of work has been done as the piston lifted the weights remaining on it. But where did this work come from? Not from the internal energy of the air because its temperature remained constant. Here the work came directly and completely from the heat which was transferred from the 100°F. constant temperature reservoir.

This last experiment may seem somewhat startling in view of earlier statements to the effect that no heat engine can change heat energy into work *completely*. Here is a process where we seem to be doing exactly that. Now the catch is this. It is true that as long as this process can continue in the manner described, all the heat entering the cylinder is converted completely into work. But it is obvious that, sooner or later, either the piston will reach the end of the cylinder, or all the weights will be removed from the piston and the pressure in the cylinder will reach zero. To make the operation of this heat engine *continuous,* some way must be found to return the piston again to its starting point. And try as hard as we will, experience has shown that it is always necessary to remove some heat from the system at some temperature lower than that at which it was added, if we are to get the piston and the air back to the starting point. Carnot, Clausius, and Kelvin were the first to perceive the fundamental implication of this, and stated it as a basic hypothesis, previously discussed in Chapter 3, called the Second Law of Thermodynamics. A little later we shall examine the line of reasoning that these great men used in discovering this limitation that nature has imposed on man's effort to get power out of heat. We are not quite ready yet, for there are some other thermodynamic elements that we must understand first.

We now have seen that work, heat, and internal energy are simply different manifestations of the same thing, energy, and the First Law of Thermodynamics[4] is the statement of how they are related. When this Law is applied to a non-

[4] There are many different statements of the First Law of Thermodynamics, which is the Principle of the Conservation of Energy as applied to finite systems. Kelvin's statement of the First Law is given on page 87.

flow system, that is, to one in which the working fluid remains in the system at all times, we express it as the Non-Flow Energy Equation,

*Heat added = change in internal energy +
work done*

or expressed in mathematical symbols, where Q = heat added in Btu, $\triangle U$ = change of internal energy in Btu, and W = work done in ft-lbs,

$$Q = \triangle U + \frac{W}{778}$$

The Greek delta ($\triangle$) is a frequently used mathematical symbol for "change in"; thus, $\triangle U$ = change in U.

Thermodynamic Properties: Pressure, Volume, and Temperature

Thermodynamics has been described as the natural science that deals with energy, transformations of energy, and the properties of matter. Thermodynamic *properties* are necessary to describe the *state* of a system. For instance, we could describe the air in our room as having a temperature of 70°F., a pressure of 14.7 lbs per sq in., and a specific volume (volume of one pound) of 13.3 cubic feet per lb. In order to analyze and study heat engine performance we must be able to determine the various properties that the engine's working fluid will have as it changes state throughout the various parts of a cycle. Then, using these properties in the appropriate thermodynamic equations, we can get solutions to the problems we are investigating. Although it is not our purpose here to do any problem-solving, we nevertheless should have a clear understanding of a certain group of thermodynamic properties, of how gases, vapors, and liquids behave in general, if we are to gain a worth-while insight into heat engine theory.

We should be aware that heat engines are essentially fluid systems in which heat and work can interact. Although many fluids can be used in heat engine systems, there are two that stand out in importance far above all others. These are steam and air. Steam still clearly dominates the power production field, although the modern steam turbine has little resemblance to the quaint *Puffing Billy* of a century ago. Air is important not because it is used in actual heat engines in its pure state, but because it can be used in idealized air-standard cycles for convenient study of internal combustion engine performance and capabilities. Air is a permanent gas throughout the range of conditions in which it is used in heat engine systems, but in different parts of the cycle steam may take the form of a gas, vapor, or liquid.

If we are to follow certain of the interactions that occur during changes of state in air systems, let us consider first the common properties of *pressure, specific volume,* and *temperature.* At first glance pressure seems to be a property that is very easy to understand, but there are some aspects of it that can be confusing. Pressure is defined as the force exerted by a fluid on a unit area, lbs per sq ft, and can be measured with many different kinds of pressure gauges. An ordinary pressure gauge measures the pressure either above or below atmospheric pressure. Above atmospheric pressure the reading would be called gauge pressure; below, it would be a vacuum of some particular magnitude. In thermodynamics, however, the pressure we are interested in is *absolute pressure,* the pressure that would be measured with a gauge if there were no atmosphere present. The diagram in Fig. 18 should be helpful in understanding these different relationships in pressure.

It should be noted here by just what mechanism a fluid can exert pressure. According to the kinetic theory of matter the force causing the pressure is due to the bombardment of molecules on the walls containing the gas. Now, if the system contained only a very few molecules, the force exerted on the walls would be finite at each point of molecular impact and zero at all other points. The pressure exerted by such a system would not be continuous with either area or time and would be useless as a property. Therefore, the systems and parts of systems that we consider are always large enough that we take account only of the average effect of a very large number of molecules. Such a system is called a continuum. In fact, the classical thermodynamics does not require any knowledge at all of the molecular structure of matter. This way of looking at things is called the *macroscopic* point of view. It is the point of view that we will follow consistently in our consideration of other thermodynamic properties and phenomena. It should be stated, however, that the behavior of a system could also be

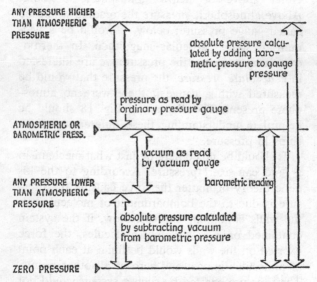

ANY PRESSURE HIGHER THAN ATMOSPHERIC PRESSURE

absolute pressure calculated by adding barometric pressure to gauge pressure

pressure as read by ordinary pressure gauge

ATMOSPHERIC OR BAROMETRIC PRESS.

vacuum as read by vacuum gauge

ANY PRESSURE LOWER THAN ATMOSPHERIC PRESSURE

barometric reading

absolute pressure calculated by subtracting vacuum from barometric pressure

ZERO PRESSURE

Fig. 18. Pressure relationships

described by summing up the behavior of each molecule and further considering all the particles of which the molecule is composed. This is another field of study known as statistical mechanics and is a very important subject. Many of the conclusions we shall reach could also have been arrived at by this alternate *microscopic* point of view.

The *volume* of a fluid system is a thermodynamic property that is easy to comprehend because it is a geometric quantity that we can see. It is expressed in units of cubic feet or cubic feet per lb. The volume occupied by one pound of a substance is called its *specific volume*.

Temperature is a property that we can feel. Objects feel relatively hot or cold depending on how much they differ from body temperature, but there is nothing basic about such a concept of temperature, nothing that suggests a method of measuring temperature with precision. Pressure is measured in units of force and length squared (lbs per sq ft), while volume is measured in units of length cubed (cu ft). Temperature, however, is different from all other properties in that it is a fundamental concept, something that cannot be measured in terms of other properties or dimensions.

Of course, we could place an ordinary blank mercury thermometer in melting ice, make a scratch on the glass stem, and call this 32°F. Then we could place it in boiling water, and when the rising mercury column became stationary, we could make another scratch and call this 212°F. Then we could make 180 equal divisions between these two scratches, extrapolate the scale below 32°F. and above 212°F., and we would have made the familiar Fahrenheit thermometer. But there is nothing fundamental about such a scale. It is altogether arbitrary, and we could have constructed it in a hundred different ways and invented a hundred different thermometers. Furthermore, we could never infer from such a thermometer that there is a minimum temperature below which it is impossible to go, or that there is a fundamental temperature scale that exists, irrespective of any thermometric substance. Also, it would be impossible to use our Fahrenheit thermometer at either very low or very high temperatures. At −38°F. the mercury would freeze solid, and above 675°F. the mercury would boil into a vapor.

We run into such problems regardless of the thermometric substance we attempt to use in the thermometer. Thomson was very much aware of this difficulty and recognized the need for a fundamental temperature scale. He was able to establish such a scale and described it in his paper of 1848. We shall see a little later just how this was done. For the time being we merely say that, on the basis of thermodynamic reasoning, Kelvin was able to show that there must be an absolute zero of temperature, and that it exists at about 460 degrees below zero on the Fahrenheit scale. Accordingly, the Fahrenheit *absolute scale* (°F. abs.), which is always used in thermodynamic equations, can be determined by adding 460 to the Fahrenheit temperature.

The manner in which *pressure (P)*, *specific volume (v)*, and *absolute temperature (T)* are related in air and other gases was established long before the time of Kelvin and Carnot—in fact, it was about the time that Thomas Newcomen was born, 160 years before Lord Kelvin. In 1660 Robert Boyle, investigating vacuums and the behavior of gases, performed a celebrated experiment in which he discovered how pressure and volume were related in gases. He published the results in "New Experiments Physico-Mechanical touching the spring of air and its effects," and stated his conclusion that the pressures and volumes of air are "in reciprocal proportions" if the temperature is held constant. This proportionality can be stated in mathematical symbols as $P \propto \dfrac{1}{v}$, or in the alternate form, $v \propto \dfrac{1}{P}$. The relationship is now known as *Boyle's Law;* in common language it says that volume decreases when pressure increases, and vice versa.

It should be obvious to everyone that temperature also affects the pressure and volume of gases. You will have noticed that tires appear somewhat deflated on a cold winter day, and that the pressure may rise several pounds when you drive at high speed on a hot road. Although the relationship between temperature and both volume and pressure is quite simple, it was not until about a hundred years after Boyle's experiment with the "spring of air" that Jacques Charles gave us the answer. He discovered that if he heated a confined quantity of any gas in such a manner that the volume could vary while the pressure remained constant, then the change in volume was always directly proportional to the change in temperature. Again this relationship can be stated in mathematical symbols as $v \propto T$, and has come to

111

be called *Charles' Law*. Later, these two laws were combined into a single relationship:

$$v \propto \frac{T}{P}$$

These symbols are a simple mathematical statement that the volume of a gas varies directly with its temperature and inversely with its pressure. We can rearrange the properties and change the expression into an equation if we introduce the constant of proportionality. Thus,

$$\frac{Pv}{T} = a\ constant$$

This is called the "equation of state" for gases.

We know now that this equation is *exactly* true only for so-called *perfect* gases; nevertheless, it is a very close approximation for many actual gases, such as air. (We shall reserve the definition of a "perfect gas" until a later point where it becomes essential to a specific discussion.) Once the value of the constant is determined for any particular gas, the equation of state is very useful in calculating properties of gases when certain other properties are known. For instance, if the air in your house is at 72°F. (72° + 460° = 532°F. abs.), and if the barometric pressure is 15 pounds per square inch (2160 pounds per square foot), you can easily calculate the specific volume, since the gas constant for air is known to be 53.3.

$$v = \frac{53.3 \times 532}{2160} = 13.1\ cubic\ feet\ per\ pound$$

Density, which is weight per unit volume, is

another property that can be determined directly from specific volume. One is simply the reciprocal of the other; thus, for the above air:

$$density = \frac{1}{13.1} = .0765 \; pounds \; per \; cubic \; foot$$

There are other thermodynamic properties with strange-sounding names, such as internal energy, enthalpy, and entropy, that are useful in understanding and analyzing thermodynamic processes. Many of these properties can be calculated through the manipulation of numerous thermodynamic equations. Others must be determined by direct experimentation whose results are listed in tables and graphs. But in any event, if we are to understand the various processes that make up the many different heat engine cycles, it is first necessary to have some knowledge of how the properties of matter change as the different forms of energy are added to or removed from it.

Thermodynamic Processes: Reversible and Irreversible

We have been talking about processes without first giving a definition of them. A process occurs when a system changes from one state to another. Thus, when we heat air in a cylinder, the temperature may rise and the volume may increase. Since some properties have changed, the state of the air has changed accordingly, and a process has occurred. There are two broad classifications of processes of interest in engineering thermodynamics. These are non-flow processes and steady-flow processes. The imaginary piston and cylinder apparatus that we have described can perform non-flow processes, those in which the working fluid remains permanently within the cylinder or boundaries of the apparatus. A flow process, on the other hand, is one in which the fluid crosses the boundaries of the engine; steam's leaving a turbine is an example. Up to the present time the experience of engineers has indicated that practical heat engines can best be built by using steady-flow cycles which always use flow processes, at least in certain parts of the cycle. The analysis of these steady-flow processes and cycles involves the use of a Steady-Flow Energy Equation, which is more complicated than the Non-Flow Equation already shown on page 105. The explanation of this added complication is that additional energy forms, such as kinetic energy of the entering fluid, flow work, and potential energy, must be taken into consideration. Fortunately, however, a substantial amount of heat engine theory can be understood through the consideration of non-flow processes alone, and for simplicity we shall limit our consideration to this type. But we must keep in mind that because of this limitation, the heat engines we describe may appear strange and impractical. Nevertheless, the general principles and conclusions at which we shall arrive will apply equally well to steady-flow heat engines.

Although it is possible to perform an infinite number of different kinds of processes on thermodynamic systems, we shall limit ourselves at present to just four non-flow processes in which the working medium is some perfect gas. In each of these four processes we shall hold some particular property constant. First we have the *constant pressure* process, in which the piston and weights move up and down as heat is added to or removed from the cylinder, thus expanding or contracting the gas. Secondly we have the *constant volume* process, where the piston is locked and the temperature and pressure of the gas rise and fall as heat is added to or removed from the system. Thirdly we have the *isothermal process,* where the temperature of the gas in the cylinder is kept constant as heat is added and work is done by lifting a piston against a decreasing pressure. And fourthly we have a process in which the piston does work because the gas expands *adiabatically* (that is, without receiving heat from any source) against a constantly decreasing pressure.

If the adiabatic process is also performed *reversibly,* we find that another unique property, called entropy, remains constant. The use of entropy in heat engine theory will be explained later. The concept of reversibility is very important in thermodynamics and is the essence of the Carnot Principle, which in turn is basic to any understanding of heat engine fundamentals.

We already have discussed reversibility very briefly in Chapter 3, but let us now digress and see whether we can get further insight and appreciation of this phenomenon. Suppose you drop a ball of putty on the sidewalk. There is little if any bounce, the putty remains on the walk, and the process can be described as irreversible. The ball's kinetic energy, derived from its velocity at the moment of impact, was dissipated within the putty in the permanent deformation of its mass. Next, suppose you drop a golf ball on the sidewalk. Now you note that the ball bounces back perhaps 80 per cent or 90 per cent of the distance through which it fell. This time the kinetic energy was not dissipated, but rather was stored momentarily in the elastic structure of the golf ball and then released to impel it in the opposite direction at nearly the same velocity. Since the ball did not quite return to its initial starting place, this process is likewise irreversible, although to a lesser degree than for the ball of putty. To make this process completely reversible, you would need a ball that was perfectly elastic, and you would have to have a perfectly rigid surface to drop it on, and a perfect vacuum to drop it through, so that air friction could not dissipate any of the energy. In other words, this process would have to occur in such a way that when it was completely reversed, there would be no remaining evidence whatever of the process, either on the ball or in its surroundings. The shape and temperature of the ball would be exactly the same as before, it would return to precisely the same height as that from where it was dropped, it would leave not the slightest mark or deformation on the floor where it landed, and there would be no air turbulence since the ball moved through a vacuum. During such an ideal process there would be a conversion of energy form from the potential energy in the ball due to its original height above the floor, to the kinetic energy at the moment of impact, and then back to potential energy as the ball returned to its original position. But nowhere would there be any dissipation or degradation of energy to less useful or less "available" forms. In other words, the process would be thermodynamically perfect, a completely reversible process.

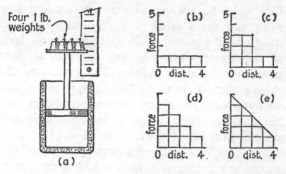

Fig. 19.

But what is the significance of the reversible process in a heat engine apparatus? To answer this question, let us perform another experiment on our piston and cylinder apparatus shown in Fig. 19a. The apparatus is so designed that the piston weighs one pound and holds four one-pound weights on its platform. The cylinder contains air, and is of such a size that removing a one-pound weight from the piston causes it to rise one foot, two pounds cause a two-foot rise, etc. With a

117

thumbscrew, or some similar device, we can produce friction against the cylinder wall and so control the rate at which the piston rises. The cylinder is insulated perfectly.

To begin then, let us slide all four weights off the piston platform. The one-pound piston will rise four feet, and the system will have produced four foot-pounds of work, 1 lb × 4 ft = 4 ft-lbs, Fig. 19b. This process is not reversible because the controlled pressure of the thumbscrew causes friction to be present as the unbalanced piston rises, and there is no way that the one-pound weight on the piston could compress the air back to its original volume. Next, suppose we start over and remove two weights. The piston now lifts three pounds a distance of two feet, at which time we remove the remaining two weights and the one-pound piston rises two more feet. We have now done eight ft-lbs of work, (3 × 2) + (1 × 2) = 8, Fig. 19c. We make a third run by sliding off one weight at a time, and now we calculate that ten ft-lbs of work have been done. (4 × 1) + (3 × 1) + (2 × 1) + (1 × 1) = 10, Fig. 19d.

It should now be evident that as smaller and smaller increments of weights are removed from the piston, and the system moves toward an equilibrium process with less and less friction, more and more work is performed by the system in expanding four feet. The ultimate limit of work performed by this process would occur when we removed infinitesimally small increments of weight, and the system would always be infinitesimally close to equilibrium. There would be no restraining action by the thumbscrew, and the piston would be frictionless in the cylinder. The maximum work done would be 12 ft-lbs, Fig. 19e. The process would be completely reversible because all infinitesimal weights could be replaced on the cylinder platform in reverse order and the entire system and apparatus returned to its initial state.

We note that the experiment produced an irreversible process when friction was produced by the thumbscrew. We could have reproduced the experiment with identical results and without using the thumbscrew if we had provided a stop in the cylinder that would have blocked the piston from moving more than four feet. In this event the system would be completely out of equilibrium if the weights were suddenly removed from the piston, since the air would be exerting a force of four pounds as opposed to the one-pound force of the piston. The result would be a rapid acceleration of the piston until it was abruptly stopped after a four-foot travel. Pressure waves and turbulence would be generated throughout the air in the cylinder, and this fluid turbulence would indicate irreversibility just as surely as the bearing friction did when we used the thumbscrew.

Reversibility in thermodynamic processes then is associated with absence of friction and with equilibrium conditions. We can define a reversible process as *one that never departs from equilibrium except by an infinitesimal amount, and in which no friction is present*. And by equilibrium we include thermal equilibrium as well as mechanical equilibrium. The isothermal process previously described, in which heat from a 100°F. reservoir was added to air in a cylinder at 100°F., is an example of a thermally reversible process. As the system expanded and did work, the temperature of the air in the cylinder dropped an infinitesimal amount[5] and heat flowed in. The process could be reversed by compressing the air in the cylinder, in which case the temperature would rise an infinitesimal amount above the reservoir temperature (100°F. + dt), and the heat would flow back into the reservoir. Any heat transfer process that involves a *finite* temperature difference across the boundaries of the system is irreversible because heat will flow only from a higher to a lower temperature. For example, the burning fuel in a power boiler may be 3500°F. while the generated steam may be only 500°F., with a resulting 3000 degrees of thermal irreversibility.

The advantages of mechanical reversibility are fairly obvious. We recognize the desirability of minimizing friction in a heat engine, or producing the maximum amount of work in an equilibrium process. The advantages of a thermally reversible process are more subtle but just as real. We shall see a little later that there would be a great theoretical advantage if we could build a heat engine in which the steam was generated at 3500°F. instead of at 500°F., but this is impossible at present because of the metallurgical limitations of steel boiler plate.

[5] Expressed in mathematics as the amount, "dt." A *finite* temperature drop would be expressed as "$\triangle$t."

The concept of the reversible process that we should gain here is that it represents the perfect thermodynamic process, one with no losses, degradation of energy, or loss of potential, in converting heat to work. We say that there is no loss in available energy. Reversible processes, however, are like anti-friction bearings in that they are impossible to produce perfectly. They exist only as ideal goals for engineers to strive for within the limitations of practicality. Carnot brilliantly conceived the idea that the reversible process was the key to the perfect heat engine, and we shall soon see how he devised the perfect heat engine cycle that was completely reversible in all its processes. But first let us try to analyze the various non-flow processes graphically to show their work energy potential, and explore how these processes can be put together to form continuously acting heat engine cycles.

The Engine Indicator and Pressure-Volume Diagrams

James Watt was the first man to develop the heat engine from the point of view of the scientist as well as of the practical engineer. He searched constantly for a more fundamental explanation of the behavior of steam in the cylinders of his steam engines, and it is remarkable that he was able to accomplish as much as he did in the era preceding the establishment of thermodynamics as a science.

121

HEAT ENGINES

One line of investigation that Watt followed was to attempt to determine the exact history of the steam as it proceeded through the various processes in his steam engine cycle. He wanted to find out how certain properties changed as he varied operating conditions. To help in this research, he invented the engine indicator, which was a device that recorded the pressure of the steam in the cylinder for any position of the piston in the cycle of operation. A modern counterpart of Watt's indicator is shown in Fig. 20a. The steam pressure in the engine cylinder is transmitted to the small spring-opposed piston in the indicator cylinder, and through a suitable linkage moves a stylus vertically in direct proportion to the pressure in the cylinder. The actual distance moved by the stylus for a given pressure change depends on the modulus of the indicator spring used. The stylus can be pressed against a specially coated marking paper on a rotating drum that is connected through a reducing mechanism to the reciprocating motion of the piston. In this way, the drum will rotate in synchronism with the reciprocating piston while the stylus traces a line that shows exactly how the pressure of the steam or gas in the cylinder varies with the volume. Such a line or path traced on the coated paper is called an "indicator card"; engineers use the cards to study performance of reciprocating engines and compressors and to adjust operation. This indicator card is, in effect, a pressure-volume diagram (*P-v* diagram), which is a very useful method of portraying non-flow processes and cycles.

For instance, suppose we attach an indicator to a heat engine cylinder that contains air at 50 pounds per square inch pressure, as represented by state (1) on the P-v diagram, Fig. 20b. If the pressure remained constant while the piston moved outward, the stylus on the indicator card would trace the path 1–2. But if the volume remained constant (the piston would not move) while the pressure decreased to 15 pounds per square inch through a cooling of the air, the path traced would be line 1–3. If, next, the volume increased during an isothermal (constant temperature) process, we should find the traced path following the equilateral hyperbola 1–4. This could be verified mathematically by noting that an isothermal expansion of a perfect gas follows Boyle's Law, which is expressed by the equation $Pv =$ a constant. We recognize this equation as an equilateral hyperbola when plotted on pressure-volume co-ordinates.

Finally, we should like to know what kind of path would be traced by a reversible adiabatic expansion of the type previously described. Here is a real problem. We recall that in this process no heat is added to the cylinder but the piston rises as the gas expands against a steadily decreasing pressure (the pressure decreases as small increments of weight are removed). We could attach an engine indicator to a cylinder where we were closely approximating such a process, and we should find the stylus tracing a line concave, downward, and at a steeper angle than that traced by an isothermal process, as shown by path 1–5

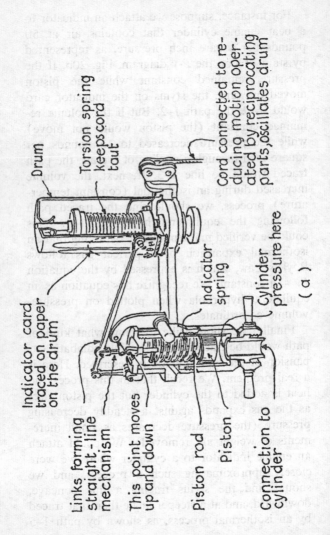

Drum

Torsion spring keeps cord taut

Cord connected to reducing motion operated by reciprocating parts, oscillates drum

Indicator card traced on paper on the drum

Links forming straight-line mechanism

This point moves up and down

Indicator spring

Cylinder pressure here

Piston rod

Piston

Connection to cylinder

(a)

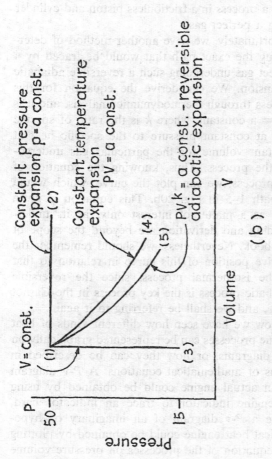

Fig. 20. Engine indicator and P-v diagram

Constant pressure expansion p = a const. (2)

Constant temperature expansion PV = a const. (4)

PV^k = a const. - reversible adiabatic expansion (5)

V = const. (1)

(3)

50

15

P

Pressure

Volume

(b)

in Fig. 20b, but this would be only an approximation. How could we find the *exact* equation of such a process in a frictionless piston and cylinder using a perfect gas?

Fortunately, we have another method of determining the exact path that would be traced by a perfect gas undergoing such a reversible adiabatic expansion. We can derive the equation for this process through thermodynamic analysis, and it is $Pv^k =$ a constant, where k is the ratio of specific heat at constant pressure to the specific heat at constant volume for the particular gas undergoing the process. Thus, knowing the equation of the process, we can plot the curve, which would be path 1–5 in Fig. 20b. This equation is given here as a matter of interest only, as its understanding and derivation are beyond the scope of this book. Nevertheless, we should remember the relative position of this curve in relation to that of the isothermal process, since the reversible adiabatic process is the key process in the Carnot cycle, and we shall be referring to it again.

Now we have seen how different kinds of heat engine processes can be represented graphically on P-v diagrams, or how they can be described in terms of mathematical equations. A P-v diagram of an actual engine could be obtained by using an engine indicator to trace an indicator card, while a P-v diagram of an imaginary or hypothetical heat engine could be obtained by plotting the equation of the processes on pressure-volume co-ordinates. In the study of heat engine performance, P-v diagrams show us a way to determine the amount of work that could be done by any particular process or cycle we might wish to try out.

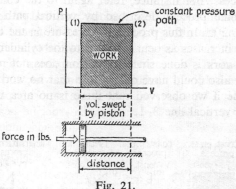

Fig. 21.

Let us examine the non-flow process shown in Fig. 21. This is a constant pressure expansion and is represented by path 1–2 on the P-v diagram. If work is defined as a force moving through a distance, then the work done by the piston is the force of the gas pressure acting on the piston face, multiplied by the distance through which the piston travels. Thus,

$$Work = force \times distance$$
$$= P \times area \times distance$$
$$since\ force = pressure \times area$$
$$= P \times v$$
$$since\ v\ (volume) = area \times distance$$

But the product of P and v can be represented as the crosshatched area shown on Fig. 21. Therefore, Work = area on a P-v diagram.

127

From this demonstration we see that area on a *P-v* diagram corresponds to work done in a constant pressure process, or in any other type of process. For instance, refer again to the constant volume process described by vertical path 3–1, Fig. 20b. In this process the pressure in the cylinder increases as heat is added to the cylinder, but no work is done since the piston does not move. We also could have determined that no work was done if we observed that there is no area under the vertical line 3–1.

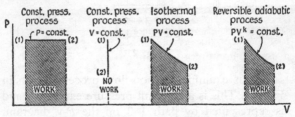

Fig. 22. Work done in non-flow processes

On the other hand, isothermal and reversible adiabatic expansions both do perform work, and we expect to be able to determine the amount of this work by calculating the area under the curve representing the particular process on a *P-v* diagram (see Fig. 22). Thus, calculating the area under a curve becomes the same problem as calculating the work done by a thermodynamic process. The equation for the process is identical to the equation for the curve, and the area under the curve and the work done can both be calculated mathematically with the integral calculus. Thus do mathematics and thermodynamics join hands in furnishing useful tools for engineers in analyzing and comparing hypothetical processes and cycles.

In this chapter we have seen how work, heat, and internal energy are interrelated, and how the state of a thermodynamic system is established by describing its properties. Furthermore, we have seen how non-flow processes can be used to produce work out of other forms of energy, how the amount of work produced will vary with each process, and how this work can be measured by determining the appropriate area on a P-v diagram. We are ready now to examine just how these thermodynamic processes can be combined to form heat engine cycles that will produce work in a useful, continuous manner.

CHAPTER 5

HEAT ENGINE THEORY; DEVELOPMENT OF THE HEAT PUMP

The Carnot Cycle and the Reversible Process

One of Carnot's great contributions was his recognition of the fact that heat engines must operate with cyclic processes. We have discussed already this cyclic nature of common heat engines, but now we should define exactly what we mean by a cycle. A cycle occurs when a thermodynamic system, having undergone a series of processes, arrives at a final state that is exactly the same as its initial state. The essential point here is that the working fluid periodically returns to the same state. In the reciprocating engines with which you may be familiar, there are pistons, valves, cams, crankshafts, and other hardware operating in a cyclic manner, but these operations are not essential parts of a heat engine cycle. The test is in the cyclic behavior of the working fluid itself.

Now what is so important about a cycle in heat engine theory? To answer this question, let us consider again our cylinder equipped with a weighted piston, and containing air as the working substance. As we have said, we could cause this apparatus to do work by simply adding heat to the cylinder and letting the expanding air do work by lifting the piston. Such a heat engine seems simple enough—what is wrong with it? Just this: the apparatus could perform work only until the piston reached the end of the cylinder. In order for this heat engine to be of any practical use, we must so design it that it can deliver work *continuously*. We could if we found a way somehow to bring the piston back to its starting point and have it then repeat the process. In other words, what we need is a heat engine cycle.

Here is where a *P-v* diagram is useful in helping us to invent such a cycle. Let us use such a diagram and start out with some arbitrary state (1), Fig. 23, and then move around a rectangle with the four processes shown.

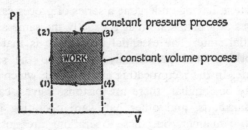

Fig. 23. *P-v* diagram for a non-flow cycle

The operation diagrammed in Fig. 23 is certainly a cycle, but is it possible or practical to build and operate a heat engine in this manner? Let us see if we can produce such a cycle with a piston and cylinder containing air as the working fluid.

PROCESS 1–2

At state (1) we lock the piston and add heat to the cylinder. The air in the cylinder now undergoes a constant volume process, and the pressure rises rapidly to state (2). At this point we add weights to the piston until the downward force equals the new pressure at state (2), and then we unlock the piston.

PROCESS 2–3

We now continue to add heat to the cylinder and the piston rises with the weights, at constant pressure, until the volume of the air has increased to state (3). Here we again lock the piston.

PROCESS 3–4

We next run some cooling water over the cylinder, removing heat and causing the temperature and pressure to drop while the volume remains constant. Then we slide the same number of weights off the piston that we added at state (2) so that the downward force again balances the lower pressure at state (4), permitting us to unlock the piston.

PROCESS 4–1

We continue to cool the cylinder, but now the piston drops at constant pressure, as the air is cooled and its volume diminishes. When we reach state (1), we stop the cooling and again lock the piston. We have now completed the cycle and are ready to start over again.

Here, at least in theory, is a useful heat engine. It continuously receives heat at high temperature, rejects heat at some lower temperature, and continuously (in cycles) does work by lifting weights to higher elevations. It is true that any prototype model that we might actually build would be of somewhat different design from the apparatus here described. But the theoretical cycle has been worked out, and now it is only a problem in practical engineering to design the hardware. For instance, instead of having a piston raise weights on a platform, we probably would connect it to a crankshaft by means of a connecting rod. The crankshaft would supply rotative work, and a flywheel could return the piston to its starting point after each power stroke (process 2–3). But we undoubtedly would conclude that the non-flow process was impractical because of the difficulty of transferring heat rapidly through the end of the cylinder. Instead, we could heat the air to its proper pressure in a separate heat exchanger and allow it to flow in and out of the cylinder through connecting pipes and proper valve action.

Before we would do all this, however, there are some additional facts we would want to know. What is the thermal efficiency of this theoretical cycle, that is, what is the ratio of the work done to the heat supplied? But even after these calculations were made, there still would be the question of just how good this cycle really is, compared to some other cycle we might invent.

As a matter of fact, we know through thermodynamic calculations that the thermal efficiency of this cycle is quite low. It would be pointless to attempt to build such an engine because there are other theoretical or ideal cycles that have a considerably higher efficiency. While we lack the background here to present the mathematical equations for justifying our pessimism, we do know that one clue to the degree of heat engine losses or inefficiency is the degree of *irreversibility* that is present in the processes making up the cycle. Let us see if we can detect the irreversible aspects of the cycle shown in Fig. 23, keeping in mind that the heat to operate the cycle comes from a *constant* high temperature source and that the rejected heat goes into the cooling water which is the *constant* low temperature receiver in this engine.

Since this is a theoretical cycle, we can assume that the piston is frictionless and that the forces opposing the gas pressure in the cylinder are mechanically reversible. Therefore, there is no loss due to irreversibility here. But when we test the cycle for thermal reversibility, we find we are in trouble. The air at state (1) is relatively cool, but becomes progressively hotter as we heat it, first at constant volume, path 1–2, and then at constant pressure, path 2–3. Actually, we would find that the air at state (3) has an extremely high temperature, and so it is obvious that our heat source must be at least this hot. Accordingly, the heat supplied during the constant volume process, path 1–2, would be thermally irreversible to a high degree, and to a somewhat lesser degree for the constant pressure process, path 2–3.

But what is the connection of this thermal irreversibility to the efficiency of the heat engine? How can we say that it contributes to a theoretical loss in potential work when the engine is theoretically frictionless and mechanically reversible? Look at it this way. Suppose that the heat were allowed to pass directly from the high-temperature reservoir to the low-temperature reservoir without passing through a heat engine at all. An example of such a process is the furnace in your house. Fuel is burned at several thousand degrees, and the resulting heat is transferred through the furnace walls to heat the air in your house at 75 degrees. Such a utilization of fuel may be necessary to keep you warm, but thermodynamically it is wasteful. Valuable high-temperature energy has been allowed to degenerate into less valuable low-temperature energy without first putting it through a heat engine and producing some work—the highest grade of energy. In other words, we have lost some available energy. When a cubic foot of gas is burned in a furnace, the burning generates about 1000 Btu of heat at high temperature; these Btu first heat our house and then dissipate through the walls to the cold winter air. Not one of these Btu is destroyed, but we have lost forever the potential or possibility of producing work with them. We might even say that our furnace was a heat engine with a thermal efficiency of zero.

Any heat engine that utilizes heat in any part of its cycle, at any temperature lower than that of the heat source, must be charged with a loss of available energy. By the same reasoning, if the heat which the engine rejects to the low temperature reservoir is at some higher temperature than necessary, this likewise results in a theoretical loss of available energy. The amount of this loss depends on the degree of temperature drop or thermal irreversibility, and the extent to which it exists around the cycle.

Sadi Carnot discovered all these things while pondering the true nature of the motive power of heat. We can imagine that once the fundamental concept became clear to him, the actual formulation of a reversible cycle was almost anticlimactic. He correctly reasoned that the following conditions must exist if a cycle is to operate reversibly between a constant high-temperature source and a constant low-temperature receiver.

(a) The process during which the system receives heat must be at a constant temperature and only an infinitesimal amount lower than the heat source.

(b) The process by which the system rejects heat must be at a constant temperature, and only an infinitesimal amount higher than the heat receiver or sink.

(c) There can be no transfer of heat between the system and either the source or receiver during the process by which the system is changing temperature.

Any cycle would be completely reversible then if it satisfied these criteria, and any engine built to operate on such a cycle would be completely reversible if it were made frictionless and otherwise mechanically reversible. The cycle that meets these conditions is the one Carnot proposed. It consists of two isothermal processes separated by two reversible adiabatic processes.

Let us see how this cycle operates in a nonflow heat engine, and how an indicator card would appear if we traced the cycle on a P-v diagram and used a perfect gas, such as air, in the cylinder. Refer to Fig. 24.

First, there is an isothermal or constant temperature expansion process represented by path 1–2 on the P-v diagram, in which conductor A is closed to conduct heat to the cylinder from the high-temperature reservoir as the piston rises against a gradually decreasing pressure and does work. Next, there is a reversible adiabatic expansion process 2–3, during which the air continues to expand against a decreasing pressure and does work, while the temperature of the air simultaneously drops to the same temperature as the receiver or low-temperature reservoir. During this process both conductors A and B are disengaged so no heat transfer can occur. The third process is an isothermal compression 3–4, during which some compression work is put back into the system while the low temperature heat (unavailable energy) is being transferred to the receiver through the closed conductor B. Note that process 3–4 is necessary because we somehow must return the piston reversibly back to its starting point to complete a cycle. Returning the piston unavoidably requires a compression of the air, and at the same time a removal of heat, otherwise the compression path would retrace the adiabatic expansion process 2–3. Finally, the fourth process must be a reversible adiabatic compression, 4–1, in which compression work is required to return the system to its exact starting point, state (1).

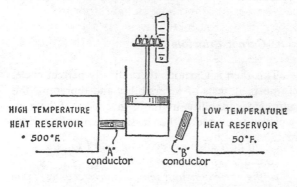

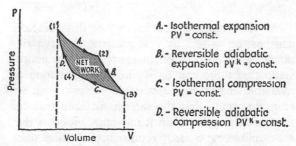

A. - Isothermal expansion
PV = const.

B. - Reversible adiabatic
expansion PV^k = const.

C. - Isothermal compression
PV = const.

D. - Reversible adiabatic
compression PV^k = const.

Fig. 24. Carnot cycle and heat engine using a perfect gas

During the expansion processes 1–2 and 2–3, work is done by the piston in an amount equal to the area under the two curves. Then, during the compression processes 3–4 and 4–1, work is put back into the system by the piston in an amount equal to the area under these two curves. The difference between these two areas is the cross-hatched area shown on the *P-v* diagram, and this represents the *net* work performed in one cycle of operation.

The Carnot Principle

This then is Carnot's theoretically perfect cycle. It meets all tests of reversibility and represents the ultimate capability in the conversion of heat to work as expressed in the classical Carnot Principle:

Of all heat engines receiving heat from the same constant temperature source and rejecting heat to the same constant temperature receiver, none can be more efficient than a reversible engine.

An acceptance of the validity of this Principle can best be gained by first grasping the true significance of the reversible process. If we understand that there can be no loss or dissipation of available energy in a reversible process, then we can understand that the same must hold true for a reversible cycle. Then it inexorably follows that a reversible cycle *must* represent perfection since to deny this would be to admit that some other more perfect cycle could somehow operate with a *gain* in available energy. But the operation of any process, cycle, or machine with a gain of potential or available energy within itself is contrary to the laws of nature as we observe them. It would mean that such a cycle or machine could, exclusively by its own action, cause a hot body to become hotter than its surroundings and a cold body to become colder than its surroundings. This possibility is inadmissible, as expressed in the hypothesis, first stated by Clausius and Thomson, that we know as the Second Law of Thermodynamics.

For those interested in following the mathematical proof of the Carnot Principle, it can be found in the appendix. This proof consists of first assuming that there is a cycle more efficient than the reversible Carnot cycle and then using it to run the Carnot engine backward. Thus the reversed Carnot engine would now operate as a heat pump and return more heat to the high-temperature reservoir than the assumed higher efficiency heat engine would require in its operation. Since such a process would result in a net flow of heat from a lower temperature region to a higher temperature region with no other outside source of energy, it would constitute a direct violation of the Second Law of Thermodynamics. Thus the assumption that any cycle could be more efficient than a reversible cycle is invalid, and the Carnot Principle is proved.

You will recall from Chapter 3 that Carnot's proof of his Principle contained a fallacy founded on his adherence to the caloric theory of heat, and that Thomson and Clausius later put the proof on the correct basis of the Second Law. Here again we can point out that the essence of Carnot's reasoning was that the reversible process by its very nature is a thermodynamically perfect process with no loss, and the *proof* of the Carnot Principle is more or less incidental. The fact that Carnot's original proof contained a fallacy was of no consequence to the fundamental validity of his basic hypothesis.

With the discovery of the perfect heat engine cycle, engineers now had a standard against which all other theoretical cycles or actual heat engines could be compared. Look back a moment at Fig. 24. It is possible to calculate mathematically the crosshatched area of the diagram for any condition of operating temperatures. The equations of the curves are known, and the limiting states (1), (2), (3), and (4) can be determined from thermodynamic equations. Thus, if a Carnot heat engine operated between two heat reservoirs, let us say, 500°F. and 50°F. respectively, we could plot its cycle on *P-v* co-ordinates, and we should find that the enclosed area of the cycle, representing the net work done, would account for 46.9 per cent of the heat received from the high-temperature reservoir. In other words, the Carnot engine would have a thermal efficiency of 46.9 per cent, and for every 1000 Btu of heat received it would produce 469×778 foot-pounds of work, and reject 531 Btu of heat to the 50°F. receiver as unavailable energy. Furthermore, *no other heat engine* operating between the same temperatures and using air *or any other fluid* as the working medium could do any better, whether operating on a non-flow or steady-flow cycle. We know this is true because of the Carnot Principle.

The earliest practical heat engines all used steam as the working medium, and so it was quite natural for Carnot and Thomson to base their calculations on ideal steam engine performance. They prepared tables that showed, among other things, the quantity of heat that could be converted into mechanical effect when passing through large numbers of different temperature ranges. Steam and steam-water mixtures do not obey the perfect gas laws, and the equations and resulting plots of their expansion and compression processes cannot be predicted with the ease and accuracy of the so-called perfect gases. Accordingly, the accuracy of these early calculations depended largely on the amount and accuracy of experimental data on steam. This is reflected in the title of Thomson's paper of 1851, presented to the Royal Society of Edinburgh, "On the Dynamical Theory of Heat, with Numerical Results Deduced from Mr. Joule's Equivalent of a Thermal Unit, and M. Regnault's Observations on Steam."

Carnot was aware that temperature was the key to high heat engine efficiency, but the exact nature of the relationship somehow eluded him. To a certain extent, it eluded Thomson, too. It remained for Clausius to show the simplicity of the functional relationship of heat engine efficiency and the temperature of the heat source and receiver. This relationship can best be demonstrated after we discuss further some of the fundamental aspects of temperature, and are introduced to that most remarkable discovery of Clausius, the property called *entropy*.

The Thermodynamic Scale of Temperature

The property, "temperature," is so interwoven with thermodynamics, heat, and heat engine theory that it is particularly important to have a clear understanding of its true nature. We already have seen that temperature is a unique property of matter in that it is a fundamental concept, not expressible in terms of other units. It is unsatisfactory, from a thermodynamic point of view, to express temperature in terms of the length of a column of mercury or alcohol in a liquid-in-glass thermometer, or as the electromotive force generated in a thermocouple. If temperature is to be used in thermodynamic equations, and as an indicator of heat engine efficiency, then it must somehow be expressible in terms of some thermodynamic function.

We should know first just what it is that temperature measures. If we look in the dictionary, we read that temperature measures the relative "hotness" of things. But this definition in reality tells us nothing, for when we look up hotness, the dictionary blandly tells us that it is something characterized by high temperature. Here the kinetic theory helps us out of our dilemma. According to this theory, the pressure of a gas varies directly with the kinetic energy of its molecules. But according to the gas laws that we have discussed, we can see that the pressure of a gas also varies directly with the absolute temperature. Therefore, we may conclude that the kinetic energy of molecules also varies directly as the absolute temperature, and is in fact what temperature actually measures. The higher the molecular agitation the higher the temperature, and the slower the molecular movement the lower the temperature becomes, until there would be no temperature or pressure at all if we could somehow cool the gas to where the molecules were frozen motionless.

This atomistic or microscopic explanation of temperature may be satisfying, in that it gives us a physical picture that we can comprehend, but it does not tell us how we can *measure* temperature in some fundamental way.

Thomson was very much aware of this perplexing problem. The answer came to him in 1848 during his pondering on the significance and implications of Carnot's reversible cycle. He had the acuity to see that here was a means of establishing a universal and absolute temperature *scale,* independent of any thermometric substance and based only on energy conversion.

To show how it is possible to arrive at an absolute scale, we shall first perform a hypothetical experiment showing that an absolute zero of temperature must exist, and then extend this line of reasoning to develop an "energy" or "thermodynamic" temperature scale.

Let us set up a small Carnot reversible engine to operate between two regions at temperatures (1) and (2) as shown in Fig. 25. Since no engine can have a higher efficiency than the Carnot engine, the ratio of heat received to heat rejected, which we express as Q_1/Q'_2, has a unique value when operating between temperatures (1) and (2).

Therefore we can say,

$$\frac{Q_1}{Q'_2} = \frac{T_1}{T_2} \quad \text{or} \quad \frac{Q'_2}{Q_1} = \frac{T_2}{T_1}$$

where T represents a property called temperature on some thermodynamic scale which is independent of any thermometric substance. Operation of the Carnot engine, you will remember, does not depend on any particular type of working fluid.

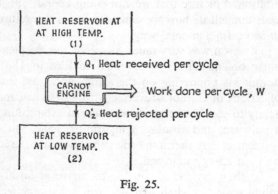

Fig. 25.

We have defined thermal efficiency of a heat engine as the work done divided by the heat received or, expressed as an equation,

$$thermal\ efficiency = \frac{W}{Q_1}$$

But according to the First Law of Thermodynamics heat energy cannot be destroyed, and therefore the difference between the heat received and heat rejected by the cycle must be the work done, $Q_1 - Q'_2 = W$. Making this substitution, then, we have,

$$thermal\ efficiency = \frac{Q_1 - Q'_2}{Q_1} \text{ or } 1 - \frac{Q'_2}{Q_1}$$

Now substituting the temperature ratio for the heat ratio as shown in the first equation, we have,

$$thermal\ efficiency = 1 - \frac{T_2}{T_1}$$

From this expression of thermal efficiency we must conclude that T_2, the temperature of the receiver, can never be zero or less than zero ($T_2 \nleq 0$). For if T_2 were equal to zero, we see that the thermal efficiency of the heat engine would be $1 - 0$, or 1, or 100 per cent. This is inconceivable, since it would result in a complete conversion of heat to work in a heat engine[1] and would constitute a violation of the Second Law of Thermodynamics. Also, if T_2 were less than zero (a negative number), the thermal efficiency would be greater than 100 per cent—the direction of Q'_2 would be reversed, and thus heat would be drawn directly from the low-temperature reservoir. This likewise would be a violation of the Second Law. So, in theory, we can approach in-

[1] Such an engine would be a *perpetual motion machine of the second kind.*

finitely close to an absolute zero of temperature but never quite attain it.[2]

Next let us continue our hypothetical experiment by operating our little Carnot engine between a high-temperature reservoir at the temperature of boiling water, T_1, and a low-temperature reservoir at the temperature of melting ice, T_2. Suppose we had some metering device that could measure the amount of heat received, Q_{steam}, and the amount of heat rejected, Q'_{ice}. If we actually were able to make these measurements, we would find that the ratio $\dfrac{Q_{steam}}{Q'_{ice}}$ would be 1.3662. But from our previous reasoning we note that this must also be the ratio of the thermodynamic temperature of these two points. Thus,

$$\frac{Q_{steam}}{Q'_{ice}} = \frac{T_{steam}}{T_{ice}} = 1.3662$$

We might decide that we wanted, let us say, 180 divisions or degrees to separate the temperature of boiling water and the temperature of melting ice. Then we have

$$T_{steam} - T_{ice} = 180°$$

Here we have two equations with two unknowns, and by solving them simultaneously we can calculate the temperature of boiling water and melting ice on a thermodynamic scale.

[2] In present-day "cryogenic" laboratories, temperatures lower than −459°F. have been achieved. This is a very small fraction of a degree above absolute zero.

$$T_{steam} = 672°F. \; abs.$$

$$T_{ice} = 492°F. \; abs.$$

When we divide the difference between the temperature of boiling water and melting ice into 180 degrees and arbitrarily assign 32° as the temperature of melting ice, we have established the Fahrenheit scale. On the other hand, if we divide this temperature interval into 100 divisions and assign 0° as the temperature of melting ice, we have the Centigrade or Celsius scale, and the corresponding Centigrade absolute zero is –273°. Temperatures on the Fahrenheit absolute scale are frequently called °Rankine, while temperatures on the Celsius or Centigrade absolute scale are usually called °Kelvin. Fahrenheit and Celsius were physicists of the 18th century, and made contributions to the field of thermometry, while Rankine was a 19th century English physicist and engineer, who made many contributions to the bridging of theoretical thermodynamics and practical steam engine design and development.

The relationship of these four temperature scales is shown in Fig. 26. Although the Centigrade scale seems the more logical one, longstanding custom has established the Fahrenheit scale as the one employed in engineering and everyday usage in the United States.

The Perfect Gas Thermometer

We now have seen how a hypothetical Carnot engine can be used to determine a fundamental

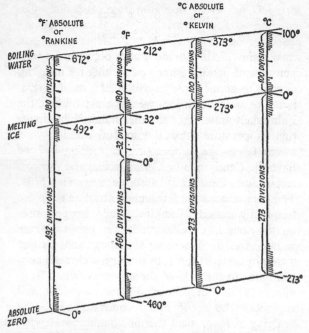

Fig. 26. Comparison of temperature scales

thermodynamic scale of temperature, but there are questions still remaining. Since we obviously cannot build an ideal Carnot engine, where did the mysterious constant 1.3662 come from? Furthermore, even though we know the temperature of the steam point and the ice point, what kind of thermometer should we use to find the thermodynamic temperature of substances in between and beyond these fixed points? You will recall that the Carnot heat engine shown in Fig. 24 used a perfect gas as the working fluid, and since the equations for isothermal and reversible adiabatic processes are known, we can calculate the net work done (area on the *P-v* diagram) for the cycle. Now, if this same gas could be used to operate a perfect gas thermometer, the results would have the same thermodynamic foundation as the thermodynamic equations from which the work of the Carnot cycle was computed.

What does a gas thermometer look like? A constant-volume gas thermometer is simply a rigid container in which changes of pressure are registered to measure corresponding changes in temperature. A constant-pressure gas thermometer, on the other hand, is one in which changes in volume are measured, in a cylinder with a movable piston, to determine corresponding changes in temperature. Diagrams of these are shown in Fig. 27.

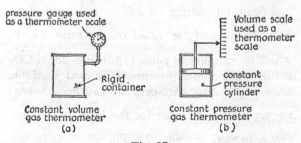

pressure gauge used as a thermometer scale

Rigid container

Constant volume gas thermometer
(a)

Volume scale used as a thermometer scale

constant pressure cylinder

Constant pressure gas thermometer
(b)

Fig. 27.

The manner in which pressure, volume, and temperature are related in perfect gases has been explained in our discussion of Boyle's Law, Charles' Law, and the Equation of State. The temperature referred to in this connection is the temperature measured by a perfect gas thermometer.

We now have a means of constructing a gas temperature scale that would be identical to a Carnot thermodynamic scale—if we could find a perfect gas. Here again we have a way out of the difficulty. From the gas laws we can define a perfect gas as one in which the volume at constant pressure, and the pressure at constant volume, both vary directly with the absolute temperature.

Stated mathematically,

$$\left(\frac{v_1}{v_2}\right)_P = \left(\frac{P_1}{P_2}\right)_v = \frac{T_1}{T_2}$$

Now suppose that we put some gas, such as carbon dioxide (CO_2), in a constant-volume gas thermometer and note its initial pressure as P. Then we place the thermometer first in boiling water and note the changed pressure, P_1, and again on melting ice and note the new pressure, P_2, to find the value of the ratio $\left(\frac{P_1}{P_2}\right)_v$, which we can plot as point (1) in Fig. 28. If CO_2 at the same initial pressure P is next used the same way in a constant-pressure gas thermometer, we get a different value for the ratio $\left(\frac{v_1}{v_2}\right)_P$, and this is plotted at point (2), Fig. 28.

The reason that points (1) and (2) are at different locations is because CO_2 is not a perfect gas. But if we continue to experiment with CO_2 and other gases, such as hydrogen and helium, at different initial pressures, we can get a sufficient number of experimental points to plot the curves shown. Studying these curves, we note that they tend to converge as the initial pressure P is reduced. We know that all gases approach perfect gas behavior as they approach zero absolute pressure, so if we extrapolate our curves to zero pressure, we find that they all converge at the point 1.3662. This number must therefore be the ratio of the absolute gas temperature of boiling water and melting ice.

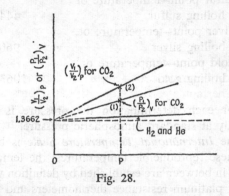

Fig. 28.

The International Temperature Scale

This technique could be used to determine the thermodynamic temperature of any substance. Our explanation here has been greatly oversimplified, and the actual determination of a thermodynamic temperature of a fixed point in nature is a highly sophisticated and expensive experimental procedure. As a matter of fact, the thermodynamic temperatures of only a few well-defined fixed points have been determined with great precision.

	°C.
1. Oxygen point—temperature of boiling oxygen	−182.970
2. Ice point—temperature of melting ice	0.000
3. Steam point—temperature of boiling water	100.000
4. Sulfur point—temperature of boiling sulfur	444.600
5. Silver point—temperature of boiling silver	960.800
6. Gold point—temperature of boiling gold	1063.000

For each determination the pressure is held exactly at standard atmospheric pressure.

The *International Temperature Scale* is based on these reproducible temperatures; the temperatures in between are established by definition when using platinum resistance thermometers and thermocouples in a certain prescribed way. This scale, with its prescribed thermometers, can be used readily and is very close to the thermodynamic temperature scale. It so happens that the mercury-in-glass thermometer, when accurately made, also can closely approximate the true thermodynamic temperature.

With a better understanding of the fundamental nature of temperature, we are now in a better position to complete our discussion of heat engine theory by an introduction to entropy and practical heat engine cycles. But before we begin, let us digress to consider another interesting ramification of Carnot's reversible heat engine.

Heat Pump Cycles and Refrigeration

We have seen that when a reversible process or cycle is operated in reverse order, all external effects are likewise reversed. Thus, if the Carnot engine shown in Fig. 25 is reversed, heat will flow from the low-temperature reservoir and into the high-temperature reservoir, while work is supplied to the engine. But this reversed heat engine is in effect a *heat pump,* a machine capable of "pumping" heat from a cold region to a hot region. Depending on how we applied such a machine, we could produce a refrigeration effect or a heating effect.

Lord Kelvin saw the fundamental similarity of heat engines and heat pumps insofar as they are both thermodynamic machines, and wrote the paper in 1852 entitled, "On the Economy of the Heating or Cooling of Buildings by means of Currents of Air."[3] In this paper Kelvin wrote more like an engineer than a physicist in that he presented the design details of a heat pump. By alternately compressing, cooling, and expanding air in a dual cylinder and piston apparatus, the apparatus could produce either a refrigeration or

[3] *Glasgow Philosophical Society Proceedings,* Vol. 3, December 1852.

heating effect. But let us read how Kelvin himself explained it.

In the mathematical investigation communicated with this paper, it is shown in the first place, according to the general principles of the dynamical theory of heat, that any substance may be heated thirty degrees above the atmospheric temperature by means of a properly contrived machine, driven by an agent (work) spending not more than $\frac{1}{35}$ of energy of the heat thus communicated; and that a corresponding machine, or the same machine worked backwards, may be employed to produce cooling effects, requiring about the same expenditure of energy in working it to cool the same substance through a similar range of temperature. When a body is heated by such means, about $\frac{34}{35}$ of the heat is drawn from surrounding objects and $\frac{1}{35}$ is created by the action of the agent (work); and when a body is cooled by the corresponding process, the whole heat abstracted from it, together with a quantity created by the agent (work), equal to about $\frac{1}{35}$ of this amount, is given out to the surrounding objects.

A very good steam engine converts about $\frac{1}{10}$ of the heat generated in its furnace into mechanical effect; and consequently, if employed to work a machine of the kind described, might raise a substance thirty degrees above the atmospheric temperature by the expenditure of only $\frac{10}{35}$ or $\frac{2}{7}$, that is less than $\frac{1}{3}$ of the coal that would be required to produce the same elevation of temperature with perfect economy in a direct process. If a water-wheel were employed, it would produce by means of the proposed machine the stated elevation of temperature, with the expenditure of $\frac{1}{35}$ of the work, which it would have to spend to produce the same heating effect by friction.

The machine by which such effects are to be produced must have the properties of a perfect thermodynamic engine, and in practice would be either like a steam engine, founded on the evaporation and re-condensation of a liquid (perhaps some liquid of which boiling point is lower than that of water), or an air engine of some kind.

Kelvin went on to calculate specific design data for an air heat pump in which air could be either heated from 50°F. to 80°F. or cooled from 80°F. to 50°F. Again in his own words:

If it be required to heat the air from 50°F. to 80°F., the ratio of expansion to the whole stroke in the egress cylinder would be $\frac{18}{100}$, the pressure of the air in the receiver would be $\frac{82}{100}$ of that of the atmosphere (about 2.7 lbs on the square inch below the atmospheric pressure), and the ratio of compression to the whole stroke in the egress cylinder would be $\frac{15}{100}$. If 1 lb of air (or about $15\frac{1}{2}$ cu ft at the stated temperature of 80°, and the mean atmospheric pressure) be delivered per second, the motive power required for working the machine would be .283 of the horsepower, were the action perfect, with no loss of effect, by friction, by loss of expansive power due to cooling in the egress cylinder, or otherwise. If each cylinder be four feet in stroke, and 26.3 inches diameter, the pistons would have to be worked at 30 double strokes per minute.

Kelvin's calculations showed that when this machine was operated as an air conditioner, in which 15½ cu ft of air per second were cooled from 80°F. to 50°F., 24.6 double strokes per minute would be required with a consumption of .288 horsepower.

Kelvin's paper may have been inspired by a desire to do something to control the temperature of the air in the British government buildings in India, which were insufferable to Englishmen not accustomed to the climate. As far as we know, his thermodynamic heating and cooling machine was never built, but we do know that it would have worked. Kelvin's device was most remarkable on two counts. First, it anticipated our present air conditioning and heat pump industry by nearly 100 years, and, secondly, it showed the power of the newly emerging science of thermodynamics to predict the performance of a reversed heat engine in an entirely new application, without building the machine and then modifying it after blind groping in trial-and-error procedures.

Early History of Refrigeration

Although Lord Kelvin was the first to approach the idea of the heat pump as a problem in pure thermodynamics, he was by no means the first to recognize the benefits of refrigeration and to investigate possible ways of supplying it. As a matter of fact, the art of refrigeration is very old indeed and was practiced long before Hero's aeolipile, the first primitive heat engine, was ever built. There are Chinese writings, earlier than the first millennium B.C., that describe religious ceremonies for filling and emptying ice cellars. The Greeks and Romans compressed snow in pits insulated with grass, chaff, and tree branches. The compressed snow was thus converted into ice for use in warmer seasons. Other ancient writings describe the Egyptians', Indians', and Estonians' methods of producing ice artificially—all similar in general principle. Shallow vessels of porous clay or some similar material were filled with water and placed on thick beds of straw at night. Under favorable atmospheric conditions of cool, dry air and a cloudless night, the simultaneous loss of heat from evaporation and radiation to the night sky caused thin layers of ice to form in the vessels by morning. The straw prevented conduction of heat from the warmer earth, and the shape of the shallow vessels with their large, exposed surfaces permitted maximum evaporation and radiation heat loss.

These early attempts to produce refrigeration, while quite primitive, were nevertheless remarkable evidence of man's ability to develop a useful art long before any rational scientific basis for the art existed. No one really knew why the porous vessels had to be placed on straw or why a cloudless night was necessary, but through intuition and the observation of cause and effect the art developed, and so the wine was cooled in the heat of the day by what must have been regarded as a miraculous process.

Many centuries passed before any significant

discoveries of physical phenomena were made that would be useful in developing artificial refrigeration. In 1607 it was discovered that a mixture of salt and ice could be used to freeze water. One hundred and forty-eight years later, Dr. William Cullen of Glasgow, Scotland, first discovered that ice could be produced mechanically by the evaporation of volatile liquids, independent of the conditions of the surrounding environment.

Dr. Cullen, born in 1710, the son of an attorney, received the finest technical education of the day at both the University of Glasgow and the College of Physicians and Surgeons in Glasgow. Graduated in 1729, he practiced for a number of years in hospitals before becoming a Professor of Chemistry and Physics at the University of Edinburgh. It was in this period that he became interested in the phenomenon of evaporating liquids under vacuums, and he performed a number of experiments in which he boiled liquids under high vacuum, using the best vacuum pump he could obtain at that time.

In 1755 Dr. Cullen published a scientific paper in Edinburgh entitled, "Essay on Cold Produced by Evaporating Fluids," in which he wrote in part:

> In an experiment made with nitrous ether when the heat of the air was about 43°F. we set the vessel containing the ether in another a little larger, containing water. Upon exhausting the receiver, and the vessels remaining for a few minutes in vacuo, we found most of the water frozen and the vessel containing the ether surrounded with a thick and firm crust of ice.

At this point we may wonder why Dr. Cullen did not immediately proceed to exploit his discovery and build machines to manufacture ice. Did he not have all the essential elements at hand? There was the refrigerant nitrous ether, which in high vacuum would boil at a low enough temperature to freeze ice. Furthermore, he had a vacuum pump that could produce a continuous vacuum. These items seem to be basically quite similar to the component parts used in our modern vapor compression refrigeration machines.

But this all seems obvious only in the light of our present-day technology and knowledge of thermodynamics. Remember that this was nine years before James Watt made his trip to Glasgow University to investigate the trouble they were having with their Newcomen engine. It was sixty-nine years before Carnot's work on the true nature of the motive power of heat was published, and nearly one hundred before Kelvin and Clausius finally resolved the great enigma of heat, work, and energy through the concepts of the First and Second Laws of Thermodynamics.

In comparison, consider the discovery made in 1834 by the French physicist Jean Peltier, in which he noted that when electric charges flow across the junction of two dissimilar metals, there is produced an absorption or liberation of heat depending on the direction of current flow. But not until today, more than 125 years later, has the Peltier principle become the subject of intense research activity in some of our largest manufacturing corporations in an effort to produce pure electronic refrigeration for competitive commercial applications. Why did they wait for 125 years? Simply because theoretical knowledge was not available until recently to exploit the development of the principle. Recent breakthroughs in the field of solid state physics have contributed to the discovery of semi-conductors that can produce the Peltier effect with higher efficiencies than previously thought possible. As a result, it is entirely possible that within a few years electronic heat pumps, in which certain types of refrigeration and heat pump systems will operate without cyclic processes or any mechanically moving parts, will be commonplace.

Dr. Cullen's paper described an interesting laboratory experiment, but future technical and scientific progress was necessary before it could be adapted to practical ends. Cullen became committed to other research projects and did nothing further to develop his ice-making process. The effect of his discovery was not lost, however, since his paper was published and available for others to use.

Other experiments and discoveries were made. About 1761 Joseph Black (1728–1799), one of Dr. Cullen's brilliant students, continued along this same general line of experimentation and developed his now famous theory of latent heat of fusion and evaporation which gave us our first insight into how heat was involved in the changing phases of matter. A few years later Joseph Priestley (1733–1804), English physicist and chemist, discovered ammonia and carbon dioxide, which later would prove to have favorable thermodynamic properties for use as refrigerants.

It is interesting to note that both Black and Priestley were intimate friends of James Watt, the man who contributed most to the early development of the steam engine. It is also interesting to note that in many respects the early development of the refrigeration industry was comparable to the development of the steam engine industry. Just as Watt, Trevithick, Evans, and others were able to make solid progress in heat engine design before all the details of thermodynamic theory were worked out, so also was substantial progress made in the practical design of heat pumps as refrigeration machines before the era of Kelvin and Clausius. It is not astonishing either that some of the early "steam engine" engineers made valuable contributions to the development of refrigeration machines, although history does not credit one man as the father of refrigeration to the extent that Watt is credited with developing the steam engine.

Watt apparently had no interest in refrigeration, but Oliver Evans, the American from Delaware, who developed the high-pressure steam engine, was probably the first to propose the closed cycle for refrigeration. His idea was suggested in a treatise published in Philadelphia in 1805. We find in some personal letters of Richard Trevithick written in 1828 a dissertation on *The Production of Artificial Cold*. However, the invention of the first vapor compression system that was destined to form the basis of our great present-day refrig-

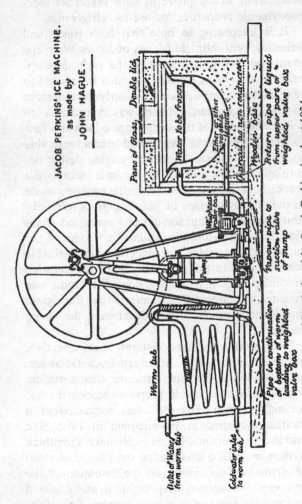

JACOB PERKINS' ICE MACHINE.
as made by
JOHN HAGUE.

Pane of Glass. Double lid.

Water to be frozen

Either or other or liquid.

Arrival of non condenser

Modern base

Return pipe of liquid from upper part of weighted valve box

Weighest valve box

Vapour pipe to suction valve of pump

Pump

Vapour pipe to suction valve of pump

Pipe in continuation of bottom of worm leading to weighted valve box

Worm tub

Cold water inlet to worm tub

Wick of Water from worm tub

Fig. 29. Ice machine designed by Jacob Perkins in about 1834

eration industry is credited to an American-born engineer by the name of Jacob Perkins.

Perkins was born in 1766 in Newburyport, Massachusetts, but little is known of his early life. We know that in August of 1834 he took out a U. S. patent for a compression machine, Fig. 29, that operated on a closed cycle in such a manner that ether was first boiled in an evaporator at low temperature and pressure to freeze water. Next, the resulting vapor was compressed and condensed back into a liquid at a higher temperature and pressure. Finally, the liquid ether from the condenser was throttled through an expansion valve back into the lower-pressure evaporator, where its temperature dropped to the initial condition and thus completed the cycle.

In his patent description, Perkins described his machine as an "apparatus or means whereby I am enabled to use volatile fluids for the purpose of producing cooling or freezing of liquids, and yet at the same time constantly condensing such volatile fluids and bringing them again and again into operation without waste."

Perkins moved to England, where his first machine was built by John Hague. The machine, while crude and primitive, was mechanically successful and was the first power-driven apparatus capable of manufacturing ice in usable quantities. Perkins took out an English patent and attempted to develop his ice machine on a commercial basis. He designed a small ice plant where block ice was frozen by circulating cold brine around cans of water. Although this basic idea was widely used to manufacture ice in later years, this first attempt did not prove to be a commercial success. The whole operation, indeed, was a flat failure. The civilized world was certainly in need of mechanical refrigeration, but the problems of financing a new industry, developing machinery and equipment for which there was no precedent, and of arranging for the marketing and distribution of the ice were complex and frustrating. Time, as well as good management and adequate capital, was required to build up a new industry, even though the need was urgent and an experimental prototype model was available. Where, then, did the industry finally develop?

The history of mechanical refrigeration seems to show that its commercial development centered in three general geographic locations, England and Western Europe, the United States, and Australia. Europe needed refrigeration for its dairy, brewing, and distilling industries, and for the importing of perishable foods. Australia was becoming a great meat-producing country and would require a refrigeration industry if it was to market its product abroad. The United States was a young and dynamic nation where inventiveness seemed to flourish. The hot southern part of the United States, where the need of refrigeration was pressing, originally obtained river and lake ice harvested in the northern states. Under the threat of civil war the South's need for an independent source of ice became apparent and accelerated the development of a mechanical refrigeration industry.

Credit for the first commercially successful refrigeration machine must be given to Dr. John Gorrie of Apalachicola, Florida. Gorrie was not a physicist or engineer, but a physician who was searching for a machine to produce ice and cool air to help treat his yellow fever patients. How he came upon the idea for his machine is not clear, but we do know that he advertised the availability of its design as early as 1844. It was several years, however, before he was able to get sufficient financial backing to build his first commercial machine. He applied for a U. S. patent, which was finally granted in 1851. Gorrie's machine differed from Perkins' in that it operated on an air cycle. The description of its operation can best be obtained by referring to his patent claims, which are in part as follows:

1. The employment of a liquid uncongealable at the low temperature at which it is required to keep the engine, to receive the heat of the water to be congealed and give it out to the expanding air.
2. The employment of an engine for the purpose of rendering the expansion of the condensed air gradual, in order to obtain its full refrigeratory effects, and at the same time render available the mechanical force with which it tends to dilate to aid in working the condensing pump irrespective of the manner in which the several parts are made, arranged, or operated.
3. Supplying the water slowly and gradually to the freezing vessels and congealing it by abstracting

the heat from its under surface, substantially as here-in set forth.

4. The process of cooling or freezing liquids by compressing air in a reservoir, abstracting the heat evolved in the compression by means of a jet of water, allowing the compressed air to expand in an engine surrounded by a cistern of an unfreezable liquid, which is continually injected into the engine and returned to the cistern, and which serves as a medium to absorb the heat from the liquid to be cooled or frozen and give it out to the expanding air.

This machine was most remarkable when we consider that Gorrie was not educated as a physicist or engineer. In some respects it was similar to Kelvin's air cycle heat pump, described earlier in this chapter, although we can well wonder on what basis it was designed. Dr. Gorrie died in 1855. His machine was not developed further in the United States, primarily for lack of a technical press to disseminate technical information. Later one of his machines was shipped to England, where it was carefully described in the *Proceedings of the Civil Engineers of Great Britain*. This publication was widely read by engineers all over the world, and, as a result, Gorrie's cold air machine formed the basis of design of many air cycle refrigeration machines. This type of equipment was successfully used for many years thereafter, particularly on the seas, and was later brought to a rather high state of perfection through the subsequent better understanding of the thermodynamic processes involved. It is interesting to note that the state of Florida has honored Dr. Gorrie by placing his statue in the national statuary hall in Washington, D.C.

Jacob Perkins' first ice machine differed from Gorrie's in that it used a condensable vapor as the refrigerating medium. Although his machine was never commercially successful, he nevertheless had by chance hit upon a cycle that was theoretically sound. His idea of producing refrigeration by first evaporating a low-temperature, low-pressure liquid, and then condensing the resulting vapor at high temperature and high pressure, became the basis of the present-day vapor-compression cycle. Perkins had little, if any, real understanding of the fundamental nature of his cycle. Joseph Black, years before, had theorized on the latent heat of evaporation and condensation, but this was over sixty years before Carnot published his unnoticed paper on the motive power of heat. It would be more than a decade later before the science of thermodynamics could explain the theory of the vapor compression cycle, its theoretical capabilities and limitations, and its basic advantage over air cycle refrigeration. In the next chapter we shall see some of these fundamental facts for ourselves.

An Australian, James Harrison, studied and improved on Perkins' idea and in 1856 and 1857 took out patents in Great Britain on a sulphuric ether vapor compression machine, Fig. 30. Harrison, like Perkins, had no education as a physicist but was a clever inventor with a genius for practical mechanics. He was also a man of influence and a member of the Legislative Council of Victoria, and was able to make the long trip to England for the special purpose of building a prototype of his first ice machine, and to apply for proper patents.

In 1859 he founded a company to manufacture his machine in Sydney, New South Wales, and two years later a limited production was started in England. Records show that the first Harrison machine built in Australia was installed in the brewery of Glasgow and Thunder, Berdigo, Victoria, Australia in 1860. It operated there for many years and was the world's first application of mechanical refrigeration to the brewing industry.

The first Harrison machine built in England was installed in 1861 in the oil refinery of Young, Meldrum and Binney of Bathgate, Scotland, for the purpose of extracting paraffin. This was the first application of mechanical refrigeration to the oil refining industry. Other Harrison machines were used to manufacture block ice, and some operated in this service for many years.

As already mentioned, the early days of the refrigeration machine paralleled in many ways the early development of the steam engine. The equipment was crude, inefficient, and broke down frequently. The early designers and builders were frequently subjected to public ridicule. Some people thought that artificial ice should be outlawed on the mistaken theory that it was unhealthful, while others asserted that it was an offense to Divine Will.

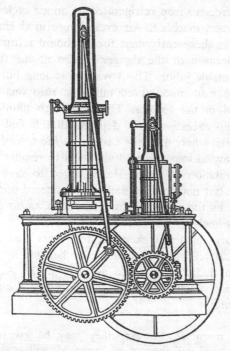

Fig. 30. James Harrison's sulphuric ether machine, with steam engine, 1859

There were accidents, too. The dangerous and inflammable ether soon gave way to ammonia and carbon dioxide, and the search continued for still safer refrigerants. Equipment failures occasionally caused the loss of whole storage rooms full of perishable products. An interesting anecdote taken from the ship's log of a sailing vessel tells of a voyage out of New Zealand with a cargo of

171

5000 frozen sheep refrigerated by an air cycle refrigeration machine. Air cycles were used exclusively in those early days for shipboard refrigeration because of the danger of fire at sea from inflammable ether. The voyage was long but no trouble was encountered until the ship was becalmed in the tropics. Then the high humidity built up excessive frost deposits that fouled the machine, whereupon the captain at the risk of his life crawled into the cold air ducts to remove the accumulation of snow. He managed to save his cargo, but not until he had been rendered unconscious by the cold and dragged out of an air duct by his heels.

Many remained skeptical for years that mechanical refrigeration could ever become an important industry. As late as 1877 a Dr. A. W. Hoffman wrote in *The Journal of the Franklin Institute*:

Ice machines, however they may be eventually improved and their effect increased, will never, in the more northern parts of the temperature zone, where a moderately cold winter with frost is generally experienced, acquire importance enough to meet the demand even approximately. They will serve merely as valuable substitutes to render us independent of the fickleness of the seasons.

This prophecy was in reference to the harvesting of ice from lakes and rivers in the winter season and storing it for summer use. In spite of this prediction, however, the practice of ice harvesting has almost vanished, while the refrigeration and air conditioning industry has grown to enormous proportions throughout the world. Indeed, it is difficult to imagine what our present civilization would be like without it. Thus, the refrigeration machine and heat pump, which are both in reality reversed heat engines, join with the heat engine to greatly raise our standard of living.

CHAPTER 6

HEAT ENGINE CYCLES AND EFFICIENCY

Entropy

One of the most remarkable contributions that Clausius made to thermodynamics was his discovery of a property that related both heat and temperature, and which he called *entropy*. Out of the earlier work of Carnot and Kelvin there had come already the realization that a useful heat engine was one that could draw heat from a high temperature source, convert a part of it into work, but then must inevitably reject the remainder as *unavailable* energy to some lower temperature reservoir. The concept of perfection of the reversible process was understood, but something still seemed to be missing. There should be some way of measuring the degree of irreversibility or loss of availability of a process or cycle. There should also be some way of measuring heat energy as a product of two properties, as we measure work energy as a product of force times distance, or of the two properties, pressure times volume change (see page 127). Heat can be thought of as having the measurable property temperature, which is a

175

driving force or potential, but we should like to have some other "extensive" property which, when multiplied by temperature, would yield the product heat.

Entropy is the missing link here, and it is so chained to the concept of reversibility, availability, and unavailability, that at least some elementary understanding of it is necessary if we are to gain any significant understanding of heat engine theory. Unfortunately, because of its abstract nature, and since we cannot relate it to our senses, entropy is usually difficult to comprehend. Nevertheless, a general understanding is possible if you are willing to use your imagination to a sufficient degree.

In Chapter 5 we saw that when a Carnot heat engine operated between some particular high-temperature source and some lower temperature receiver, the ratio of heat added to the heat engine to that rejected by the heat engine always has a unique value. We were able to establish a thermodynamic temperature relationship:

$$\frac{Q_{in}}{Q_{out}} = \frac{T_{in}}{T_{out}} \text{ (refer to Fig. 25, page 146)}$$

Clausius noted this relationship and rearranged the equality as follows:

$$\frac{Q_{in}}{T_{in}} = \frac{Q_{out}}{T_{out}} \quad \text{or} \quad \frac{Q_{in}}{T_{in}} - \frac{Q_{out}}{T_{out}} = 0$$

This simply states that the quantity of heat added to a Carnot heat engine during one complete cycle of its operation, divided by the thermodynamic or absolute temperature at which it is added, is equal to the quantity of heat rejected during the same cycle divided by the temperature at which it is rejected. Obviously, if these two quotients are equal to each other, then the difference between them must equal zero for the complete cycle. From this relationship Clausius concluded that the term $\frac{\triangle Q}{T}$, which indicates a small quantity of heat either added or removed from a system, divided by the absolute temperature at which it is added or removed, must be a *property,* since it meets the test of a property; namely, when a thermodynamic system, such as air in a cylinder, undergoes any cycle of operation and returns to its exact initial state, all the properties of the system such as temperature, pressure, and volume likewise return to their initial points and the net change in their respective values is zero.

At this point we may say yes, the expression $\frac{Q_{in}}{T_{in}} - \frac{Q_{out}}{T_{out}} = 0$ has been shown to be valid for the Carnot cycle, but this is only one particular cycle—how about other cycles? If $\frac{\triangle Q}{T}$ is indeed a property, then the net change in its value must be zero for *any* cycle.

Clausius overcame this limitation by showing that *any* reversible cycle, such as the one drawn on the *P-v* diagram, Fig. 31a, could be dissected by a large number of lines or paths representing reversible adiabatic processes, Fig. 31b. Then he reasoned that each two adjacent adiabatic paths could serve as a part of a miniature Carnot cycle. These would correspond to paths 2–3 and 4–1 as illustrated in Fig. 24, page 139. But we also note in Fig. 24 that the Carnot cycle requires two isothermal or constant temperature paths, 1–2 and 3–4, to connect the two reversible adiabatic processes. Now it is unlikely that the isothermal paths of each small dissecting cycle shown in Fig. 31c would agree exactly with the corresponding path of the cycle on which it was superimposed, and we therefore would find that we were adding and rejecting heat $\triangle Q$ along some zigzag path as shown. But if we make the Carnot cycles quite small, we can see that the zigzag path would approximate the path of the original arbitrary cycle, and since we have already seen that $\dfrac{Q_{in}}{T_{in}} = \dfrac{Q_{out}}{T_{out}}$ for any Carnot cycle, then the summation of all the terms $\dfrac{\triangle Q_A}{T}$ along path A from state (1) to (2) must equal the summation of all the terms $\dfrac{\triangle Q_B}{T}$ along path B from state (2) to (1). This can be stated mathematically as follows:

$$\sum_1^2 \frac{\triangle Q_A}{T} = \sum_2^1 \frac{\triangle Q_B}{T}$$

(The symbol Σ [sigma] means "the sum of.")

Now if we can stretch our imagination further, we can see how these paths would become *identical* if we used an *infinite* number of Carnot cycles, each requiring the addition and rejection of an *infinitesimal* quantity of heat, stated symbolically as *dQ*.

But how do we add up an infinite number of infinitesimal quantities? Impossible as this may seem, it can be done very neatly by using a branch of mathematics called the integral calculus. Since solving problems of this nature is beyond the scope of this book, suffice it to say that it is only

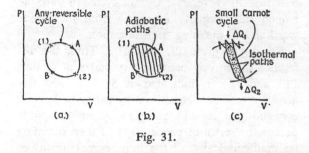

Fig. 31.

necessary to express *dQ* as a function of *T*, that is, we must be able to express how the heat is added or removed in terms of its absolute temperature, to determine the sum of all the infinitesimal terms $\frac{dQ}{T}$. This procedure is called integration. The mathematical symbol used is $\int \frac{dQ}{T}$ and it is called the integral of *dQ* over *T*.

Thus, the integral *dQ* over *T* for the reversible path *A* from state (1) to (2) is equal to the integral of *dQ* over *T* for the reversible path *B* from state (2) back to state (1). Stated mathematically,

179

$$\int_1^2 \frac{dQ_A}{T} = \int_2^1 \frac{dQ_B}{T} \quad \text{or} \quad \int_1^2 \frac{dQ_A}{T} - \int_2^1 \frac{dQ_B}{T} = 0$$

In this manner Clausius showed mathematically that $\int \frac{dQ_{rev}}{T}$ represented a change in a property of *any* system undergoing any *reversible* process. The process must be reversible because the entire structure of our reasoning to this point has been based on the reversible Carnot cycle. In 1865 he named this property *entropy*,[1] from the Greek word τροπή, meaning transformation.

Entropy is given the symbol S. Thus, the difference in entropy between two states of matter, (1) and (2), is indicated as $S_2 - S_1$, and this quantity can be determined numerically by first connecting states (1) and (2) by *any* reversible process or series of processes, and then summing up mathematically all the infinitesimal quantities of heat transfer occurring in the process, divided by the absolute temperature at which each occurs. Thus,

$$S_2 - S_1 = \int_1^2 \frac{dQ_{rev}}{T}$$

We can also write this equation another way, if we consider only an infinitesimal part of the process. In this case an infinitesimal change in entropy equals an infinitesimal transfer of heat

[1] R. Clausius, Veber verschiedene fur die Anwendung bequeme Formen der Hauptgleichungen der mechanischen Warmetheorie, Poggendorffs Annalen, Vol. 125, 1865.

during a reversible process divided by the absolute temperature. Thus,

$$dS = \frac{dQ_{rev}}{T}$$

Rearranging this equation we have,

$$dQ_{rev} = T \times dS$$

This is a mathematical statement of the fact that the rate of heat transfer in a reversible process is equal to the absolute temperature times the rate of entropy change, or in other words, the product of two *properties*. This equation suggests that temperature and entropy might be used as co-ordinates for a temperature-entropy (*T-S*) diagram, Fig. 32, much in the same manner that pressure and volume have been used as co-ordinates for the *P-v* diagram. (Fig. 21, page 127.)

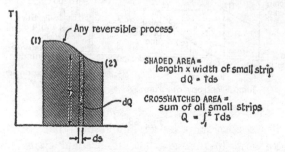

Fig. 32. Temperature-entropy diagram

But whereas area represented *work* on the *P-v* diagram, area now represents *heat* on the *T-S* diagram. This graph may be somewhat difficult to comprehend if we insist on wanting some physical picture of the phenomenon, but if we realize that entropy is an abstract concept that has no physical significance, we stop trying to comprehend it in these terms, and instead accept it simply as a property important to the understanding of the thermodynamics of heat engines.

We have previously stated that entropy is a measure of the irreversibility of a process. Let us now perform an experiment with a piston and cylinder apparatus, Fig. 33b, to illustrate how this works. Suppose the cylinder contains air at room temperature and 100 lbs per sq in. pressure, shown as state (1) on the T-S diagram, Fig. 33a.

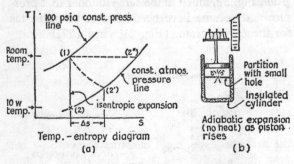

Fig. 33.

If the piston is allowed to rise reversibly and adiabatically by successively removing *infinitesimally small weights,* in the manner previously described in Chapter 4, the temperature drops to state (2), while the pressure drops to atmospheric pressure.

Since this is a reversible process the entropy change can be calculated by the equation,

$$S_2 - S_1 = \int_1^2 \frac{dQ}{T}$$

But since this is an adiabatic process, dQ equals zero, and therefore $S_2 - S_1$ also equals zero. In other words the entropy has remained unchanged for this reversible adiabatic process. This is also called an isentropic (constant entropy) process. Note that there is no area under path 1–2, as we would expect, since no heat transfer occurs in an *adiabatic* process.

Next let us insert a partition with a hole in it in the cylinder as shown in Fig. 33b, and then place a *small number of large weights* on the piston. Now as we remove these large weights one at a time, and let the system expand adiabatically down to atmospheric pressure, we find that less work is done (Fig. 19, page 117). This is because the process is no longer reversible, due to unbalanced forces and the throttling action of the restrictive orifice. We also find that the final temperature of the air is not as low as that reached in the previous experiment and that the entropy has now significantly *increased* to that shown at state (2′). Note that a dotted line connects state (1) and (2′). This does *not* represent the exact path of this process since the process is not reversible and therefore the path is not defined. All we know about this process is that it starts at state (1) and ends at state (2′). Remember that on a *T-S* diagram area represents heat only when measured under a path representing a *reversible* process. The process from state (1) to (2′) represents an increase in entropy but is nevertheless *adiabatic*.

Now finally let us use a partition with a very small pinhole, through which the air can slowly throttle and expand against a *weightless* piston. This process is completely irreversible as the air expands down to atmospheric pressure. No work is done since no force opposes the expansion of the air. The final temperature of the air is the same as its initial temperature, since no energy has been removed, but the entropy now increases to a maximum at state (2″).

Here we have seen how entropy can be used as a measure of the degree of irreversibility of a process. Wherever irreversibility occurs, entropy inevitably increases, and at the same time the availability of energy in the system diminishes. Accordingly, we lose forever any chance of producing work from this energy, and this principle, remember, applies to thermal as well as to mechanical irreversibility. For example, let us drop a marble at 200°F. into a pan of cold water at 35°F. The marble will cool down, and its entropy will decrease, while the water will heat up slightly and its entropy will increase until the combined marble and water system comes to equilibrium. At first glance we might expect that these two quantities would be equal. Certainly we know that the energy is conserved and that the heat lost by the marble exactly equals the heat gained by the water. Not so, however, with the entropy. Its value for the combined system in equilibrium will be *higher* than the sum of the entropies of the original constituent parts. Here again entropy measures the loss of *available* energy due to the irreversible transfer of heat from the hot marble to the cold water. In theory we could have inserted a little heat engine between these two objects and produced some work while the heat transfer proceeded reversibly. Had we done this, there would have been no loss of available energy, and the entropy of the combined system would have remained constant. But, of course, we didn't, and so we lost forever the opportunity of producing this work.

These ideas are incorporated in one of the corollaries of the Second Law of Thermodynamics, known as the Principle of the Increase of Entropy. This states that the entropy of an isolated system will always increase if any irreversible processes occur. For instance, the best that we can ever expect, even in theory, in a continuously operating heat engine is for the entropy of the engine and its surroundings to remain constant. But in any actual engine there inevitably will be some friction, turbulence, and unwanted irreversible heat transfer, and they will result in a relentless forward march of entropy.

Clausius pondered the significance of all this and extended this line of reasoning to not only our world and solar system, but to the entire cosmos. He concluded that "the energy of the universe is constant, but the entropy of the universe increases towards a maximum." Thus he came to the dismal conclusion that the universe was running down and some day would become lifeless at the point of maximum entropy. Whether Clausius was correct in his prediction, no one knows, of course, but many think that he made an unwarranted extrapolation of knowledge from observable data to vast and little understood phenomena. Be that as it may, the fact remains that the property entropy plays a very useful role in the analysis and understanding of small finite systems such as heat engines.

Our consideration of the function of entropy will be limited in this book to the "macroscopic" point of view employed by the classical thermodynamics. In passing it is interesting to note, however, that entropy also has a most important place in the "microscopic" view of statistical mechanics. Here we view a thermodynamic system as a myriad of molecules moving at different velocities and colliding with each other in a random manner. Entropy can be used to measure the state of disorder of these molecules. It is highly improbable that the high-velocity molecules in a gas would ever by themselves separate into an area away from the slower molecules. If this did happen, it would result in a *decrease* in disorder and an increase in the availability of the system, since now there would exist a hot region (high-velocity molecules) and a cold region (slow molecules) with the potential for producing work. The effect of all this would be to *decrease* the entropy of an isolated system and thus violate the entropy principle. Our experience shows that the expected and probable result of all fluid turbulence, throttling action, or mixing at different temperatures is a state of higher molecular disorder and thus *increased* entropy.

J. Willard Gibbs, the outstanding American physicist, who was born in 1839, just 17 years after Clausius, and who made great and significant contributions to this new science of thermodynamics in his own right, was the first to suggest the importance of using the temperature-entropy diagram for representing and analyzing thermodynamic processes. We have seen already how reversible processes can be plotted on such a diagram and why area under such a path is equivalent to the heat transferred during the process. Let us now see how we can use this to understand the true nature of heat engine efficiency as a function of temperature alone.

Temperature and Heat Engine Efficiency

We recall the operation of the Carnot heat engine performing on a non-flow cycle, Fig. 24, Chapter 5. Let us now see how this cycle would appear if we traced its four processes on a temperature-entropy diagram, Fig. 34.

First, heat is added reversibly to the cylinder at constant temperature T_H. Accordingly, the entropy of the air in the cylinder increases from state (1) to state (2) as shown. Next the air in the cylinder expands reversibly and adiabatically until the temperature drops to T_L. But this is the same as the isentropic (constant entropy) process shown in Fig. 33a. Therefore we draw path 2–3. Next the unavailable heat energy is rejected from the cylinder at temperature T_L during the reversible isothermal process 3–4, and the entropy decreases by exactly the same amount as it increased in the first process. Finally, the cycle is closed when the air is compressed isentropically back to the initial pressure and temperature, process 4–1.

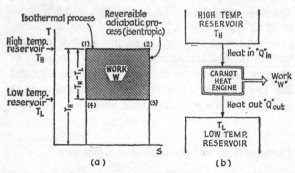

Fig. 34. Carnot *heat engine* cycle on a temperature-entropy diagram

Note that there has been no net entropy increase in the system and its surroundings. Energy has been converted from heat into work through the lifting of weights, but there has been no loss in *available* energy: All the high-temperature heat used from the high-temperature reservoir could be restored exactly by using the work already produced to drive the engine in reverse as a heat pump. This then is a perfect heat engine.

Note also that heat added during the isothermal process 1–2 is represented by the total area under line 1–2, and the heat rejected during process 3–4 is likewise indicated by the area under line 3–4. But the difference between the heat supplied and the heat rejected can only be accounted for as the work done, and this is the crosshatched area shown in Fig. 34.

We have previously defined thermal efficiency of a heat engine as the ratio of the work done to the heat supplied, or expressed by symbols:

$$\eta = \frac{W}{Q_{in}}$$

But we see by inspection that this is the same as the ratio of the crosshatched area in Fig. 34, to the total area under line 1–2. Furthermore, since all Carnot cycles must be in the form of a rectangle on T-S diagrams, we also see by inspection that the ratio of these areas must always be proportional to the distances $T_H - T_L$ and T_H. Therefore, from the geometric configuration of the Carnot cycle on a T-S diagram, we have:

$$\eta = \frac{T_H - T_L}{T_H}$$

where T_H and T_L are the thermodynamic or absolute temperatures of the heat source and receiver, respectively. To illustrate, if we had a source of heat at 1000°F. (1460°F. abs.) and a low-temperature reservoir at 70°F. (530°F. abs.), it would be theoretically possible to design a heat engine with the following efficiency:

$$\eta = \frac{T_H - T_L}{T_H} = \frac{1460 - 530}{1460} = 63.7\%$$

Thus the thermal efficiency of a *perfect* engine is shown to be a function of *absolute temperature only,* and note that this analysis has made no limitation as to the type of fluid used in the heat engine. It applies equally to liquids and vapors as well as to perfect gases. Although Carnot was aware that the maximum "motive power" of a heat engine was a function of temperature, he was unable to perceive the exact nature of that function. It remained for Clausius to be the first to show the classic simplicity of the above equation.

Engineers from this time on knew the fundamental nature of the problem in heat engine design. They could see now the theoretical advantage of lowering the temperature at which some proposed heat engine would reject heat, as well as the advantage of supplying heat at the highest possible temperature. But whereas the temperature of heat "receivers" is limited by the temperatures of naturally occurring agencies of nature about us, such as the atmosphere, well water, river water, etc., there is much less theoretical restriction on the use of higher temperature sources of heat. In this regard the only present limitation is our ability to develop metals and other materials that can withstand the high temperatures of burning fuels and still retain their durability and structural strength. This remains the most challenging problem today in the continuing development of heat engines. Recent developments in this field have made possible the design of extremely high-temperature jet engines and rocket motors, and many research agencies are working hard to increase further the working life, reliability, and efficiency of these modern heat engines.

We have already seen how Lord Kelvin hit on the idea of operating a heat engine in reverse and thus using it as a heat pump. We might assume logically that the maximum theoretical performance of such a machine could also be expressed as a function of temperature, similar to our calculation of maximum heat engine efficiency. Let us see how this can be done.

If the Carnot heat engine is reversed, the heat and work quantities simply reverse their direction, and the cycle traced on the T-S diagram now moves in an opposite or counterclockwise direction, Fig. 35. Now work must be put into the heat pump, with the result that heat Q_L will be "pumped" from the low-temperature reservoir, and heat Q_H will be transferred into the high-temperature reservoir. If the effect we are trying to achieve is that of *refrigerating* an area below the temperature of its surroundings, as in a kitchen refrigerator, a cold-storage locker or a room air conditioner, we call the reversed heat engine a refrigeration unit or compressor. In this case the refrigeration effect is represented by the crosshatched area Q_L, and the work required to produce this effect is shown by the crosshatched area W, Fig. 35a.

On the other hand, the effect we want may be

that of using the reversed heat engine as a *heating* machine. In this case we commonly call the reversed heat engine simply a heat pump, although, in the context of thermodynamics, a heat pump should include *any* reversed heat engine. The heating effect Q_H, now desired, is represented by the total area under path 1–2, and this includes both crosshatched areas in Fig. 35a. The work required remains the same, area W.

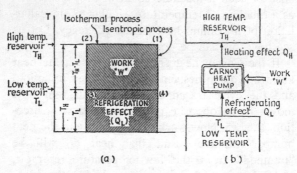

Fig. 35. Carnot *heat pump* cycle on a *T-S* diagram

In the operation of heat engines, we are striving to *convert* heat energy into work, and the degree to which we are successful in doing this we express as thermal efficiency. With refrigeration units and heat pumps, however, we are not striving for a maximum conversion of energy from one form to another. Instead, we are trying only to pump a maximum amount of heat with a minimum amount of work, and the ratio of the effect desired to the work required to produce this effect is designated as coefficient of performance (C.P.). Thus, for a refrigeration unit,

$$C.P._{Ref} = \frac{Q_L}{W} = \frac{T_L}{T_H - T_L} \text{ (Fig. 35a)}$$

and for a heat pump,

$$C.P._{HP} = \frac{Q_H}{W} = \frac{T_H}{T_H - T_L}$$

As an example, suppose we wish to determine the smallest amount of work that would be necessary to operate a deep-freeze unit at 0°F. (460°F. abs.) in a room at 75°F. (535°F. abs.). We can quickly calculate the coefficient of performance:

$$C.P._{Ref} = \frac{T_L}{T_H - T_L} = \frac{460}{75} = 6.13$$

This equation says that for every unit of work energy we put into the compressor, we can *in theory* pump 6.13 equivalent units of heat energy out of the deep freeze.

As another example, suppose we wish to heat our house at 75°F. with a heat pump using the outside air at 0°F. as the heat source. Again calculating the coefficient of performance, we have:

$$C.P._{HP} = \frac{T_H}{T_H - T_L} = \frac{535}{75} = 7.13$$

In words, the theoretical heating effect we can get out of this heat pump is 7.13 times the equivalent units of electrical energy we supply to it to operate the compressor motor. This does not mean, of course, that we are creating energy, but we are in a sense getting something for nothing. To explain, suppose we had 5 kilowatts of electricity available to heat a room. We could use it directly in an electric heater and produce 5 × 3413 or 17,065 Btu per hour.[2] On the other hand, we could use these 5 kilowatts to operate a heat pump motor, and in this case it would be theoretically possible to get 7.13 × 17,065 or about 121,500 Btu per hour heating effect. The gain in Btu might be the difference between heating a single room or an entire house. In this case the energy pumped from the outside air at 0°F. would be free for the taking, but the total energy balance would still be conserved. This can be seen by referring to Fig. 35b. The heating effect Q_H would equal 121,500 Btu per hour, which would be 7.13 times as great as the electrical work input W, but the difference between Q_H and W would exactly equal the heat Q_L drawn from the 0°F. reservoir.

Remember, though, that these figures represent the maximum conceivable performance of a *perfect* heat pump, in which there is no irreversibility or net entropy increase, a condition that cannot be reached in practice. Actual heat pumps operate at lower coefficients of performance, just as actual heat engines operate at thermal efficiencies below the Carnot value.

[2] One kw. = 3413 Btu per hour.

Thermodynamic Properties of Water and Steam

For more than 150 years, from the days of Thomas Savery's fire engine to after Carnot, almost all heat engine progress developed around steam. Efficiencies were poor, progress slow and uncertain. In retrospect this lag is understandable in view of the anemic state of heat engine theory. In this light it is remarkable that the steam power cycle has continued in basically the same form from Watt's day to the present and, furthermore, continues to supply the world with more power than any other heat engine or other agency. The modern steam power cycles are the great central station power plants that generate electricity for use in homes and industry, around this country and around the world. It is true that the steam turbine has replaced the steam engine as the prime mover, and that the boiler, condenser, controls, and auxiliaries have been designed to a very high state of perfection and sophistication, but with all the modifications, the basic cycle is still there and probably will be with us for many years to come.

Up to this point we have limited our development of heat engine *theory* to perfect gas systems. We have seen some uses of the gas laws, a demonstration of various processes using air as the working medium, and the establishment of the thermodynamic temperature scale on the basis of a perfect gas thermometer. However, there is nothing in the concept of the reversible Carnot heat

195

engine that limits the working medium to a perfect gas. Admittedly, we used air in the cylinder as we described the processes of the Carnot cycle, but we did it for convenience only. Since we knew the equation of both the isothermal and the reversible adiabatic processes for perfect gases, we could plot their paths on pressure-volume co-ordinates and thus draw the cycle on the P-v diagram. Then, by integrating areas under these curves, we could determine the work done and the thermal efficiency for the cycle.

There is no such limitation, however, on drawing the paths of the Carnot cycle on a temperature-entropy diagram. It always will have the general shape of a rectangle regardless of the type of fluid used as the working medium, and, as already demonstrated, its thermal efficiency will always be a function of absolute temperature.

Therefore, since steam has been so important in heat engine development, we need to know more about it. We should have some understanding of how it behaves as it changes state and undergoes different kinds of processes. The behavior of steam will also show us how the various vapor refrigerants, such as ammonia, behave, and will help us to understand the refrigeration and heat pump cycles.

Everyone knows that water freezes into ice at 32°F. and boils into steam at about 212°F. If we put water in a pressure cooker, it will boil at a somewhat higher temperature. In general, we recognize that steam behaves like a gas. General information of this type was certainly known back in the days of James Watt, but accurate and complete knowledge of steam properties and behavior was lacking. Watt himself carried on careful experiments in an attempt to find out some of the basic facts he needed to understand and improve his steam engine. A generation after Watt's death, the French scientist, Henri V. Regnault, compiled the first comprehensive tables on the properties of steam. It was this work that Thomson referred to when he wrote his 1849 paper entitled, "Carnot's Theory of the Motive Power of Heat with Numerical Results Deduced from Regnault's Experiments on Steam." Since Regnault's time much research effort and money have gone into the determination of steam and water properties with greater and greater accuracy. Steam does not follow the perfect gas laws, and its equation of state is quite complicated. Accordingly, highly sophisticated experimental techniques are necessary to obtain accurate knowledge. This work has been done, and today the various properties of steam are known with great precision and are published in book form, called *Thermodynamic Properties of Steam,* or simply *steam tables.*[3]

With the aid of the steam tables, then, let us try to get an organized picture of how steam and water behave as heat is added to or removed from them at different temperatures and pressures. This can best be done by performing another hypothetical experiment with our piston and cylinder apparatus.

[3] J. H. Keenan, and F. G. Keys, *Thermodynamic Properties of Steam.* New York: John Wiley & Sons, Inc., 1936.

To start with, let us fill the cylinder with water at 70°F. and let the weight on the freely moving piston be standard atmospheric pressure, 14.7 psia. Next, let us apply heat to the cylinder but keep the pressure constant on the piston. We now observe that the temperature of the water slowly rises and that the piston also slowly rises because the volume of the water expands slightly. At 212°F. we note that the temperature of the water remains constant as heat continues to be added, but now the volume increases rapidly as the water boils into steam. After the last drop of water evaporates into steam, any further addition of heat will result in a further continuous rise in the temperature of the steam.

Let us now stop for a moment and define some terms. Water at its boiling temperature (212°F. for a pressure of 14.7 psia) is called *saturated water*. Water below its boiling temperature is called *subcooled water*. A mixture of water and steam is simply called a *mixture*. Steam at the boiling temperature is called *saturated steam,* and steam heated above the saturation temperature is called *superheated steam*.

It would be useful here to see what kind of path the above process would trace on a *T-S* diagram Fig. 36. The subcooled water initially at 70°F. is shown at state (1). Heating at constant pressure causes both the temperature and entropy to increase as shown by path 1–2. At state (2) the water is saturated, and continued heating causes the entropy to increase at a constant temperature of 212°F., until the water boils into saturated

steam at state (3). The amount of heat required
to go from state (2) to state (3) is called the
latent heat of vaporization, and is equal to 970.3
Btu per lb at 14.7 psia. Continued heating of
saturated steam again causes both temperature
and entropy to increase as the steam becomes superheated, as shown by the constant pressure
path 3–4.

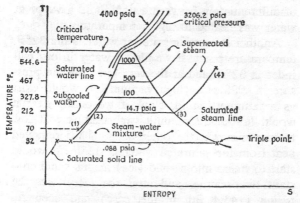

Fig. 36. *T-S* diagram for steam and water

Suppose that we now repeat the same experiment, but with a weight on the piston such that the
pressure is 100 psia. In this case we find that the
boiling point of the water is raised to 327.8°F.
and the latent heat of vaporization reduced to
888.8 Btu per lb. Continued experimentation
with higher and higher pressures would give us the
results shown in Fig. 36. The boiling point would
continue to rise, as the pressure was increased,

until a *critical point* was reached, at which state the latent heat of vaporization would be zero. The critical temperature and pressure as read from the steam tables is 705.4°F. and 3206.2 psia, respectively. It is possible, of course, to generate steam at even higher pressures than this, but then there would be no latent heat of vaporization nor observable change of phase from a liquid to a vapor. In fact, there would be no observable point of differentiation between a liquid and a vapor as water was heated to higher temperatures.

Another interesting state for water is the 32°F. temperature point. If we placed water in our cylinder at 32°F. and at the very low absolute pressure of .088 psia (high vacuum), it would exist as a saturated liquid. Now, if we added heat it would *boil at 32°F.* until vaporized at that low temperature. On the other hand, if we removed heat from the saturated water at 32°F., it would start to freeze into a solid (ice) at this same constant temperature, and after the *latent heat of fusion* (143.4 Btu in this case) had been removed, the temperature of the ice would again start to drop. The *triple point* for water is 32°F., as it is the temperature at which water can coexist in the three phases of solid, liquid, and gas. Below 32°F. there is no saturated liquid line, and water can exist only as ice or water vapor, as shown in Fig. 36. This is why water vapor in the air changes directly into snow during winter storms, and why snow or ice can evaporate (sublimate) directly into vapor on a cold winter day.

With this introduction to the behavior of water

and steam let us now analyze its behavior in steam power cycles, from the thermodynamic point of view.

Ideal Vapor Cycles in Heat Engines and Heat Pumps

As we have already seen, the ideal reversible cycle as proposed by Sadi Carnot was a non-flow cycle, impractical for a useful heat engine. Long years of experience have shown engineers that heat engines can best be built through the use of steady flow processes. In these processes the working medium flows through the prime mover in a steady stream, and the various processes performed on the working medium to complete the cycle may occur in different pieces of apparatus connected by pipes.

We recall that the very earliest steam engines of Savery and Watt operated this way. Steam was generated in a separate *boiler;* the steam was then piped to a cylinder, where it was used to produce either a vacuum or a pressure directly on a piston. This cylinder and piston with the associated mechanism and flywheel was the *prime mover,* which was the second essential apparatus in the cycle. Watt added the condenser as a third and separate piece of apparatus. He reasoned correctly that this arrangement was much more efficient than if he tried to condense the steam in the cylinder itself. The condensed steam was then piped out of the condenser to a fourth and final apparatus, a *con-*

densate pump, from where it was injected back into the boiler.

Now over two centuries later this is still the basic arrangement of steam power cycles, and is called the Rankine cycle, after the same English physicist and engineer for whom the Rankine temperature scale is named. A simplified schematic flow diagram of the Rankine cycle is shown in Fig. 37.

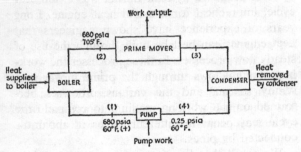

Fig. 37. Flow diagram of the Rankine cycle

But although the basic concept is still the same, it is true that there have been important modifications of this cycle, and that boilers operate today at much higher pressures and temperatures than Watt ever dreamed of. High-strength alloy steels and advanced engineering design make this possible. The fuel is fired in the boiler furnaces with coal stokers or automatic gas, oil, or powdered coal burners, with high combustion efficiencies and at enormously high heat-release rates. The prime mover in the modern Rankine cycle is usually a high-speed steam turbine, designed through the application of fundamentals in dynamics, strength of materials, and fluid mechanics, and built with the great precision made possible by today's machine tools. Condensers are designed with full knowledge of the fundamental laws of heat transfer, and they are marvels of compactness and high-performance efficiency. These changes have been made not only to increase the horsepower of heat engines, but, more important, to narrow the gap between actual performance and the maximum theoretical performance of the Carnot engine. Let us now see how this progress has evolved and just where we stand today.

It is quite helpful to analyze the Rankine cycle with the aid of a temperature-entropy diagram. We can trace the various processes shown in the flow diagram Fig. 37 on such a diagram, and thus get a direct comparison of this cycle with the theoretical Carnot cycle. But now, since our thermodynamic fluid is water and steam, we must show the position of the cycle in relation to the saturated liquid and saturated vapor lines as shown in Fig. 36. The result is the cycle shown in Fig. 38.

Let us start with the condensate as it leaves the pump and enters the boiler, state (1), Figs. 37 and 38. We note that its temperature is 60°F., since this is the temperature at which it left the condenser, and its pressure is 680 psia, since this is the boiler pressure against which the condensate pump must operate. The process from state (1) to state (2) is a constant pressure process in the boiler. To draw this process on a T-S diagram, we must first refer to the steam tables to find out

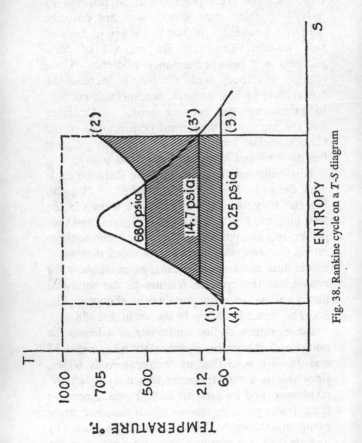

Fig. 38. Rankine cycle on a T-S diagram

what the boiling temperature of water is at a pressure of 680 psia. We determine that this is 500°F. and accordingly draw in path 1–2, similar to the constant pressure paths shown in Fig. 36.

What has happened in the boiler is simply this. Subcooled water at 60°F. was injected into the boiler and heated until its temperature rose to 500°F. At this point it became saturated and started to boil at constant temperature. The resulting saturated steam left the boiler drum and entered some superheating tubes, where it was further heated at the same constant pressure until its temperature rose to 705°F., state (2), Figs. 37 and 38.

The superheated steam at 680 psia and 705°F. is now piped out of the boiler and into a steam engine or turbine, where it does work by expanding reversibly and adiabatically against a piston or turbine wheel to some lower pressure. Since the entropy remains constant for this process, the resulting path 2–3 is vertical on the *T-S* diagram. The exact location of state (3) will depend, of course, on the pressure at which the steam is exhausted from the prime mover. The heat engine flow diagram given in Fig. 37 is for a condenser capable of condensing the exhaust steam at 60°F. The steam tables tell us that the absolute saturation pressure corresponding to 60°F. is only 0.25 psia, and so we find state (3) on this pressure line in Fig. 38.

Suppose, however, that our condenser temperature had been 212°F. In this case the corresponding saturation pressure is 14.7 psia (standard atmospheric pressure), and now the steam expansion through the prime mover would have stopped at state (3'). Would there be any advantage in stopping the expansion at state (3')? There are indeed some practical arguments for doing this. There would be no problem of keeping air out of the condenser, as is the case where a high vacuum is present. As a matter of fact, it would now be possible to eliminate the condenser entirely and discharge the exhaust steam to the atmosphere as Evans did in his early "steam puffers." But note the price we would have to pay for this simplification of design. We would lose the available work represented by the crosshatched area between the 14.7 psia path and the 0.25 psia path, Fig. 38.

Therefore, if 60°F. cooling water should be available, we would want to use it in the condenser as shown. The steam would then be condensed along path 3–4, and saturated water would leave the condenser at state (4) and go to the condensate pump. The pump now compresses the water isentropically from state (4) to state (1), during which the temperature rises very slightly, as shown.

Thus we have completed the cycle on a T-S diagram. The total area under constant pressure path 1–2 represents the heat supplied to the boiler, while the area under constant pressure path 3–4 represents the heat taken away from the condenser. The difference between these areas is the total crosshatched area which represents the useful work of the cycle,[4] and the thermal efficiency is the ratio of this area to the total area under path 1–2 representing the heat supplied.

Suppose we now compare the thermal efficiency of this Rankine cycle with the Carnot cycle. We first must know the temperature at which the fuel burner can supply heat to the boiler. The actual flame temperature of burning coal, gas, or oil may be between 3000°F. and 4000°F., but no metal pipe or heat transfer surface available today could continuously withstand such high temperatures and still maintain the necessary boiler strength. So because of metallurgical limitations, we unavoidably must squander large amounts of the available energy locked in our natural fuel reserves. But suppose we compromise and try to utilize this heat at 1000°F. Metals glow red at this temperature, but some alloy steels still maintain reasonable strength.

Assuming then that we could design a heat engine to operate between the temperatures of 1000°F. (1460°F. abs.) and 60°F. (520°F. abs.), we know that the maximum conceivable thermal efficiency could not exceed that of the Carnot cycle shown as the dotted rectangle in Fig. 38. This efficiency is:

$$\eta = \frac{T_H - T_L}{T_H}$$

$$= \frac{1460 - 520}{1460} = 64.4\%$$

[4] More accurately, the crosshatched area represents the work of the prime mover minus the pump work. The pump work is quite small and can be ignored in this case.

207

Note that 60°F. is taken as the lowest probable condensing temperature available in naturally occurring water reservoirs such as rivers, lakes, or well water. Actually, river water usually rises above this temperature in the summertime in most parts of the country, and well water might be either too expensive to use or not available in the large quantities needed. We might argue that colder condensing water might be supplied if we first used a refrigeration unit to cool it. Such a scheme would get us nowhere, however, since the work required to operate the refrigeration machine would be more than the additional work produced in the heat engine. There can be no trick method of bypassing the Second Law of Thermodynamics.

What problems would we face if we attempted to design a Rankine cycle heat engine to operate with a boiler temperature of 1000°F.? A glance at Fig. 36 shows us that the critical temperature of steam is 705.4°F., and its corresponding critical pressure is slightly over 3200 psia. Therefore, a boiler operation at 1000°F. would be entirely above the critical point. In this range no part of the constant pressure path occurs at constant temperature, and so an isothermal addition of heat would be virtually impossible to achieve, notwithstanding the formidable design problems of supercritical pressures.

For such reasons most modern central-station power plants are designed on cycles that are modifications of the Rankine cycle. Pressures rarely reach the critical pressure, and superheat temperatures—state (2), Figs. 37 and 38—rarely exceed 1000°F. One modification is known as regenerative feed water heating. The boiler feed water is heated in stages, from the condenser temperature to the boiler temperature, by bleeding small amounts of steam from the turbine at appropriate temperatures. In effect, this reduces the high degree of thermal irreversibility that occurs when the relatively cold condensate is injected into a hot boiler.

The over-all thermal efficiency of the conventional modern steam power plant today is likely to be between 25 per cent and 40 per cent. This efficiency may seem somewhat disappointing in view of the theoretical possibilities demonstrated by the Carnot cycle in the previous equation. Remember, though, that this is still a far cry from the very low efficiencies of the crude steam engines of Watt, Evans, and Trevithick. Furthermore the practical limit has not yet been reached; research and development continue.

The Binary-Vapor Cycle

Engineers from the time of Watt have toyed with the idea of using some fluid other than water in steam power cycles. Carnot commented on this possibility but concluded that it was extremely unlikely that "nature would provide a suitable substitute." What properties would we look for in searching for an ideal fluid? It should have a very high critical temperature and relatively low saturation pressures at temperatures around 1000°F. On the other hand, we would like to have its saturation pressures above atmospheric when its condensing temperatures were below 100°F., so that we could eliminate the problems of maintaining high vacuums. The fluid should be chemically stable, non-corrosive, non-toxic, and should have certain other desirable thermodynamic characteristics.

As Carnot predicted, this path of investigation and development has not proved to be very fruitful. One development along this line should be mentioned here, however, as it has had some limited success in a few highly specialized power plants. It is known as the *binary-vapor* cycle.

In this cycle two fluids, mercury and steam, are used in such a way that each fluid undergoes a conventional Rankine cycle. Mercury has a high critical temperature, and its saturation pressure at 1000°F. is only about 180 psia. Unfortunately though, its saturation pressure is very low at ordinary condensing temperatures; an extremely high vacuum in the condenser would occur if we attempted to use mercury in a single Rankine cycle. However, it may be used to good advantage in an arrangement shown in Fig. 39. Mercury is heated in a boiler and then passed through a mercury turbine and mercury condenser. The mercury is condensed at the high temperature of 500°F., which permits a manageable condenser pressure, and at the same time this rejected heat can be used to *supply* heat to a *steam* boiler, which is used in a conventional steam cycle as shown.

The thermodynamic advantage of this cycle is that most of the heat drawn from the high-temperature source (the fuel burner) can be utilized isothermally at the very high temperature of 1000°F. while the unavailable energy still can be rejected isothermally at the low temperatures of the conventional steam condenser. This isothermal supply and rejection of heat, you will recall, is a necessary condition in order to obtain the reversibility in the Carnot cycle. The advantage of the binary-vapor cycle can be clearly shown by

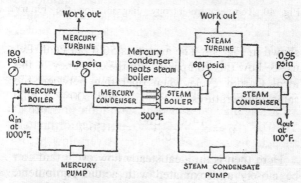

Fig. 39. Flow diagram for the binary-vapor cycle

plotting it on a *T-S* diagram, Fig. 40. We note that the combined mercury and steam cycles fit closely into the Carnot rectangle drawn between the 1000°F. and 100°F. temperature limits. From the properties of steam and mercury and by using the appropriate thermodynamic equations, we can accurately calculate the thermal efficiency of the ideal binary-vapor cycle at the design condition

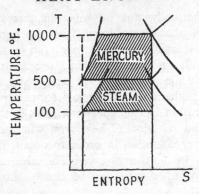

Fig. 40. Temperature-entropy diagram for the binary cycle

shown in Fig. 39. The answer is 56.6 per cent. Let us see how this compares with the efficiency of the ideal Carnot cycle when operating between the same temperatures of 1000°F. and 100°F.

$$\eta = \frac{1460 - 560}{1460} = 61.6\%$$

Here then is an ideal steady flow cycle that can be closely approximated with actual equipment, built with available engineering materials and with proven engineering techniques, and that comes reasonably close to the Carnot efficiency at the high heat source temperature of 1000°F. Nevertheless, and in spite of its theoretical advantage, the diminishing returns of the high initial cost of the binary cycle, together with certain operating difficulties, have limited its application.

Engineering progress in recent years has produced other types of heat engines that can utilize very high-temperature heat. We shall investigate some of these in our next chapter. But before we conclude our study of thermodynamics, we should examine, from a theoretical point of view, how the reversed heat engine or heat pump has evolved as the basis of the great refrigeration and air conditioning industries.

The Vapor Compression Cycle

We have seen that both heat engines and heat pumps[5] developed historically in a similar pattern. Crude machines were built by ingenious men long before the fundamental processes were understood or adequate theories worked out. Even the machinery components were similar in many respects. Both employed cylinders with reciprocating pistons, both circulated thermodynamic fluids such as steam, air, or some special refrigerant, and both required heat transfer equipment such as boilers, condensers, evaporators, and cooling coils.

Then, in the middle of the 19th century, the theoretical foundations were laid for understanding the conditions under which heat could be converted into work and mechanical refrigeration could be produced. Long-standing mysteries were suddenly clarified, and it was discovered that heat

[5] Heat pumps may be called refrigerators, refrigeration machines or compressors, condensing units, air conditioners, room coolers, or heat pumps, depending on the application. Actually, they are all *heat pumps* in a thermodynamic sense.

engines and heat pumps were essentially the same thing.

Prior to this time two general types of heat pumps had been built in very limited numbers and in a very crude form. One type used air as the thermodynamic medium while the other type used a volatile liquid such as ether. Air cycle heat pumps had one obvious advantage—the refrigerant used was absolutely safe. Obviously, air is nontoxic and non-flammable, and safety was of paramount importance in some types of applications. But thermodynamics later showed that there were some theoretical objections to the air cycle heat pump. Let us see now what these were.

In Fig. 35 we saw how a process of the perfect reversible Carnot heat pump could be represented as a rectangular cycle on a T-S diagram. First, heat is taken from a cold reservoir at constant temperature (isothermal process), then the gas or vapor is compressed reversibly and adiabatically (isentropic process) to a higher temperature, next heat is transferred to the high-temperature reservoir, again at constant temperature, and finally the cycle is completed by expanding the thermodynamic fluid reversibly and adiabatically back to its starting point. This, then, is how a *perfect* heat pump can operate, one that will have the maximum conceivable coefficient of performance. Note that there is no limiting condition in the analysis of the Carnot cycle that specifies the type of fluid that must be used. The only condition is that the cycle must be reversible and must consist of two isothermal and two isentropic processes. Thus, either a gas, such as air, or some condensable vapor, such as ether or ammonia, could be used.

In designing an actual refrigeration machine, however, we are faced with the problem of producing a *practical* machine. Just as in the case of heat engines, engineers have concluded through long experience that the most suitable way to build a heat pump for practical applications is as a steady-flow device, in which each process of the cycle is performed in a separate piece of equipment. Thus if air were used as the refrigerant, a logical arrangement of equipment would be as shown in Fig. 41a. Air could be expanded isentropically through an expansion turbine to some lower pressure and temperature, process 1–2. This cold air would then pick up heat (refrigeration effect) by flowing through a coil at constant pressure, process 2–3. Next the air would be compressed isentropically in a turbocompressor to some higher temperature, process 3–4, and finally heat would be removed from the cycle by passing the air through another heat exchanger at constant pressure, process 4–1.

This is certainly a practical cycle, one in which the component parts could be arranged in a suitable form for convenient use. Heat exchangers and turbocompressors can be designed and manufactured without difficulty, and the expansion turbine could help drive the turbocompressor if placed on the same shaft as shown.

But how does this compare with the ideal Carnot heat pump? The comparison can best be shown by drawing the cycle on a *T-S* diagram,

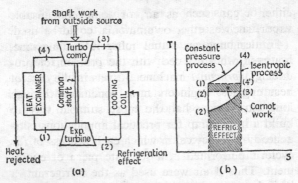

Fig. 41. Air compression refrigeration cycle

Fig. 41b. Both the expansion process, path 1–2, and the compression process, path 3–4, can closely approach the reversible adiabatic (constant entropy) path. In other words, there is no *theoretical* reason that these processes cannot be isentropic, as in the Carnot cycle. However, when heat is added to air at constant pressure, the temperature rises rather sharply. Likewise, when heat is removed, the temperature drops. Therefore, our constant pressure processes 2–3 and 4–1 are *not* isothermal and depart from the ideal Carnot cycle. This, then, must be a compromise between the theoretical advantage of transferring heat isothermally, and the practical simplicity of using a heat exchanger where the air flows through at constant pressure.

But exactly what is the theoretical thermodynamic objection to using the constant pressure rather than the constant temperature processes? We can explain it this way. The air at state (2) must be considerably colder than the refrigerated area that we are serving, while the air at state (4) must be considerably hotter than the cooling water or other reservoir to which we are rejecting heat. This results in thermal irreversibility and a resulting loss in coefficient of performance. This loss can be clearly shown by referring to the *T-S* diagram, Fig. 41b. The refrigeration effect is represented by the crosshatched area under path 2–3, while the net work required is shown by the area enclosed by the cycle 1–2–3–4–1. But a Carnot cycle would be represented by the dotted rectangle 1–2′–3–4′–1, and we can see at a glance that not only would the required work be reduced by the two triangular-shaped areas, but the refrigeration effect would also be increased by the amount of the triangular-shaped figure 2–3–2′.

It was this theoretical limitation, together with some other objections, that accounted for the gradual elimination of the air compression cycle as a serious competitor to the vapor compression cycle many years ago. Let us now see how the vapor cycle of Jacob Perkins ultimately proved to be superior.

From a thermodynamic viewpoint there are two reasons why it is advantageous to use readily condensable vapors as refrigerants. One reason is that these vapors, just like water, change phase[6] at constant *temperature* while heat is added to the saturated liquid at constant pressure, or while heat is removed from the saturated vapor at constant

[6] This is a term used to describe the change of a saturated liquid to a saturated vapor or vice versa.

pressure. We can duplicate the isothermal processes of the Carnot cycle while condensing a vapor or boiling a liquid in conventional, steady-flow, constant-pressure heat exchangers. Another reason is that a liquid at high pressure, unlike air, will drop sharply in temperature when throttled to some lower pressure. We can eliminate the expander turbine, which was a necessary and rather expensive component of the air cycle. In its place we can now substitute an inexpensive throttle valve or expansion valve, as it is called in the trade.

A simple flow diagram for the vapor compression cycle is shown in Fig. 42a. And its corresponding cycle on a T-S diagram is shown in Fig. 42b. Its sequence of operation is described as follows:

A saturated liquid is first throttled from the high-condenser pressure and temperature to the lower evaporator temperature and pressure as shown by process 1–2. Note that this is a completely irreversible adiabatic process, and so the exact path cannot be shown on a T-S diagram. That is why a dotted line connects states (1) and (2) in Fig. 42b. The entropy has increased as shown, but the area under the dotted line has no significance. Note too that the refrigerant has changed from a saturated liquid at state (1) to a mixture at state (2), since a part of the liquid has flashed into a vapor as the temperature dropped.

After leaving the expansion valve, the mixture is piped to an evaporator, where the remaining liquid boils at constant low temperature and pressure[7] until becoming a saturated vapor at state (3). This process produces the refrigeration effect shown by the crosshatched area in Fig. 42b. The saturated vapor is then drawn into a compressor, where it is compressed isentropically along path 3–4. During this process the vapor is superheated, and when it enters the condenser at state (4), it first must be desuperheated until it again becomes a saturated vapor and then is condensed the rest of the way at constant temperature as shown by path 4–1.

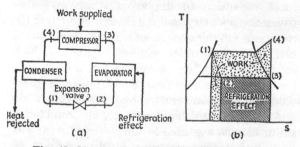

Fig. 42. Vapor compression refrigeration cycle

The entire area under path 4–1 represents heat rejected from the cycle, and therefore the difference between this area and the crosshatched area representing refrigeration effect, represents the work required. We can see from an examination of the T-S diagram that this area is still somewhat greater than a corresponding Carnot rectangle

[7] For example, liquid ammonia boils at –28°F. when at atmospheric pressure, and ammonia vapor condenses at 80°F. when at 153 lbs per sq in. absolute.

would be, but the theoretical advantage over air should be apparent. The coefficient of performance theoretically possible with the vapor compression cycle depends on a number of factors, such as the type of refrigerant used, the amount of superheating that occurs, and the various ways that this elementary cycle can be modified. How successful it has been is evidenced by the fact that today it clearly dominates all the other forms of refrigeration combined.

One of the reasons for this domination was the success in finding better refrigerants. With the rapid expansion of the vapor compression refrigeration industry, much research effort was directed toward this end. Ether was highly inflammable; carbon dioxide required extremely high condensing pressures; ammonia was widely used for many years and had many favorable thermodynamic characteristics but was highly toxic and also inflammable under certain conditions; sulfur dioxide was used to some extent, but it was toxic and highly corrosive in the presence of moisture.

It was not until 1930 that Dr. Thomas Midgley announced to the scientific world the discovery of a group of chemical compounds called halogenated hydrocarbons,[8] which not only had the necessary thermodynamic and chemical properties to make them desirable refrigerants, but also were non-toxic and non-flammable. This development gave the refrigeration and air conditioning indus-

[8] More popularly known under the trade names of Freon, Genetron, etc.

tries a tremendous boost as it permitted the use of vapor compression equipment in homes and public buildings, with perfect safety. Because these refrigerants are so safe, they have found wide use in the so-called "aerosol bombs" which are now used to dispense hundreds of products, from insecticides to tooth paste.

So much for our brief study of the thermodynamic foundation of heat engines and heat pumps. But before we close our story let us see what progress has been made in heat engine development during the past century, and after the period of Carnot, Kelvin, and Clausius. What has the development been in areas other than steam and what is the outlook for the years to come?

CHAPTER 7

HEAT ENGINE PROGRESS AFTER CARNOT, KELVIN, AND CLAUSIUS

Internal Combustion Engines

Carnot perceived quite accurately the theoretical advantages of using air as the working medium in a heat engine (see page 71). He also correctly predicted some of the serious problems that needed to be overcome.

Some early experimentation with hot air engines was carried out by various engineers, using a heat exchanger to heat the air in a manner similar to the boiler in a steam power plant. But the results were monotonously the same—the heat exchanger burned out in the high temperatures. Although the fuel was the same as burned in steam boilers, there was no similar protection against overheated metal surfaces. In steam boilers the walls are protected by the boiling water, whose temperature will never be higher than the saturation temperature corresponding to the pressure of the steam. Thus, while the combustion of fuel occurs at several thousand degrees, boiling water remains at a relatively low temperature, being only 545°F. at the very high pressure of 1000 pounds per square inch.

Carnot suggested in his paper that this difficulty could be overcome by "heating the air directly by combustion carried on within its own mass," thus eliminating the necessity of transferring heat *through* a heat exchanger wall. This is the principle of the internal combustion engine, and experimentation and development of this type of heat engine were not long in coming. In 1833, W. L. Wright built the first internal combustion engine, in which pressure from the burning charge acted on a piston face to produce the motive force. Five years later William Barnett worked out a method for compressing the air-fuel mixture before ignition, so that the subsequent expansion would recover more of the available energy from the charge. In his paper of fourteen years earlier Carnot had suggested the experiment. It should be understood, however, that Wright's and Barnett's machines were only crude experimental models and in no sense had any commercial value. Actually, very little is known about them, and they contributed little to engine development although they did apparently incorporate certain sound ideas.

For some years internal combustion engine development remained in the realm of ideas; it was not until 1860 that a commercial model first appeared on the market. In that year the French inventor J. J. E. Lenoir began producing an engine that used illuminating gas for fuel and operated much on the principle of a double-acting steam engine. It employed a two-stroke cycle, in which a gas mixture was drawn in and ignited during one stroke, and the burned combustion products then pushed out of the cylinder during the return stroke. The engine developed little power and apparently had a thermal efficiency of only about 4 per cent. Nevertheless, several hundred of these models were sold.

Notwithstanding these earlier inventions and patents, there is another man who stands out clearly as the great pioneer of the gasoline engine and the unquestioned founder of the gasoline engine industry. His stature in the field of internal combustion engines compares to the position of Watt in the development of the steam engine. He was Nikolaus August Otto (1832–1891) of Cologne, Germany. Although Otto never received a technical college education, he was an inventive genius with an ability to organize his inspirations into realities. He associated with, and obtained the support of, other men who were technically trained engineers and entrepreneurs, and through team work and organization he laid the foundation of our great automotive and gas engine industry.

Records show that Otto's first experiments were performed in 1861 with an "atmospheric" gas engine similar to the Lenoir design. Basically this engine consisted of a cylinder and piston with a valve arrangement that permitted an explosive mixture of gas and air to be drawn in as the piston moved outward in the cylinder. Then at the proper point in the outward stroke, the mixture was ignited and the resulting heat increased the gas pressure on the piston face and gave it a further push outward. Otto noticed that the exact time that ignition occurred in the outward stroke of the piston was a critical factor in performance of the engine. If it occurred too soon, the cylinder charge was too small and the piston was not pushed all the way to the end of the stroke, or "top dead center," as it was called. If it occurred too late, other problems resulted. Otto found that a better effect was produced by first drawing in a charge and then compressing it back before ignition. Here in his own words is the way that he recorded his observations:

Taking the quantity of mixture sucked in with a quarter of the piston stroke, I observed that the piston only seldom passed the dead centre. After each effect it arrived near the end of its stroke and was then pulled back in the same way. After the first trials of starting the engine had failed, I knew the cause thereof; the burnt gases cooled down much more than I had calculated. I altered the machine in such a way that I could suck in the explosive mixture on one-half and even three-quarters of the piston stroke. At half charge the small engine continued running, at three-quarters charge its operation was even worse, which again was easy to explain. I then found the right idea; ignition and combustion must take place at the beginning of the piston stroke, and this idea was at once successful. I sucked in explosive mixture to one-half and eventually three-quarters, tried to press the piston back as far as possible by turning the flywheel back-

wards, then I ignited and behold, the flywheel vig-
orously rotated several times. That was the starting point of a four-stroke gas engine. In that very
year the drawing of such an engine was completed.

But Otto was unable to bring out a successful
four-stroke cycle engine at that time. The stresses
produced by the violent explosions of the compressed charge were so great that the experimental
engine was destroyed, and he found himself without funds to continue. At this point he joined
forces with Eugen Langen, a technically educated
engineer with financial resources, and together
they decided to develop the two-stroke cycle engine since it showed more promise of practical
success. This effort did prove successful, and resulted in the first Otto and Langen engine.

A heavy piston operated in a cylinder open at
the top, and the reciprocating motion of the piston was transmitted to a rotating shaft and flywheel by a toothed rack engaging a gear fastened
to the shaft. The gear turned freely when the rack
moved up but produced a turning motion on the
shaft through a clutch when the rack moved
down. The design of this clutch was Langen's main
contribution. The motive force was produced as
follows: An explosive charge of gas and air was
drawn into the cylinder as the piston moved half-
way through its upward stroke. The charge was
then ignited, and the freewheeling piston was
driven up, the inertia of its heavy weight carrying
it to such a point that a vacuum was produced
in the cylinder. Then the pressure of the atmos-

phere acting on the top of the piston forced it down, and caused the rack, gear, and clutch mechanism to turn the shaft in the proper direction. It is interesting to note here the similarity of this design to Newcomen's original steam engine; both used atmospheric pressure to drive the power stroke of the piston.

This first Otto engine was heavy and noisy, and the rack-and-pinion drive was basically a poor design, but nevertheless the device showed an operating efficiency twice as high as the Lenoir engine. So in 1872 the firm of Gasmotoren-Fabrik Deutz A. G. was formed, with Otto as the managing director, and production was started on engines with capacities up to 3 horsepower. About 5000 units were produced.

Despite commercial success, Otto was not satisfied with this first design and began agitating for development of his four-stroke cycle engine that had shown such interesting possibilities in his first experiments, back in 1861. His business associates, however, opposed this plan; they were more interested in staying with what they felt was a sure thing. It was wiser, they argued, to direct development efforts toward elimination of the awkward rack-and-pinion gear drive, substitution of a direct crankshaft connection, and other minor improvements.

Otto, however, would not be diverted. He independently started construction and tests on his resurgent four-stroke cycle engine and this time, with the years of experience behind him, brought out an engine that was immediately successful. It produced 3 horsepower and ran at 180 revolutions per minute. It was relatively quiet in operation and became known as the "Otto Silent."

As a matter of fact, Otto's new engine was so superior to all other existing models in both performance and efficiency that it quickly dominated the internal combustion engine industry. Competitors, taken by surprise, had to move fast or face economic ruin. Concerted attempts were made to attack Otto's patents, and the technical literature was carefully searched for evidence of prior discovery. Such a paper was found to have been published in 1862 in Paris by the French engineer Beau de Rochas, at almost the exact time when Otto conducted his original experiments. In his paper Beau de Rochas proposed a theoretical four-stroke cycle having the following sequence of operation:

1. Suction of the charge into the cylinder during the entire outstroke of the piston.

2. Compression of the charge during the following instroke.

3. Ignition at dead center and expansion during the next outstroke (power stroke).

4. Forcing the burned gases out of the cylinder during the following instroke, thus completing the cycle.

This paper effectively described the operating cycle of Otto's silent engine, and this evidence, together with certain other exhibits, convinced the courts of Germany and France that Otto's patents should be nullified. The English courts, however, ruled that the Otto patent should remain valid on the basis that the Beau de Rochas paper had remained unknown and unexploited. Regardless of the legal hairsplitting and patent rulings, history now accords Otto the honor of being the inventor of the four-stroke gas engine, and the driving force behind the establishment of the great internal combustion engine industry. At the time of his death in 1891 more than 30,000 Otto cycle engines were in operation, some with multicylinder designs and with ratings up to 100 horsepower.

Now, over seventy years after Otto's death, the reciprocating gasoline engine still dominates the internal combustion engine field, particularly in the automotive industry. The basic four-stroke Otto cycle is still pre-eminent although, of course, many improvements have been made in such features as spark ignition of the charge, valve design, advancement in lubrication and machine design techniques, etc., to permit smooth and quiet operation at high rotative speeds.

The sequence of operation of a modern Otto cycle engine is shown in Fig. 43. Each cylinder of the engine contains an intake and exhaust poppet valve that are operated at the proper instant by cams on a camshaft. A poppet valve is the type that rises vertically from its seat against an opposing spring that automatically closes the valve when the opening force is removed. The camshaft is geared to the crankshaft and operates at one-half the crankshaft speed so that the valves will open and close once for every two engine revolutions. Compare the four strokes shown in Fig. 43

with the four steps proposed by Beau de Rochas in 1862 and note that they are exactly the same. Thus the basic soundness of the four-stroke cycle[1] has stood the test of time for a hundred years.

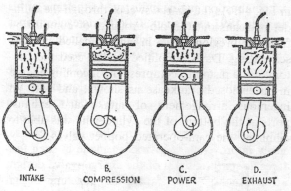

A.	B.	C.	D.
INTAKE	COMPRESSION	POWER	EXHAUST

Fig. 43. The Otto cycle

One disadvantage of the four-stroke cycle engine is the fact that the crankshaft must make two revolutions for each power stroke. The first two-stroke cycle engines of Lenoir and Otto had a power stroke for each revolution, but they were atmospheric engines and did not compress the charge before ignition. It was inevitable that someone would attempt to work out a design that could combine both two-stroke operation and the compressed charge. Such an engine was first developed by Sir Dugald Clerk of Scotland in 1878, and it

[1] More often called a "four-cycle" engine today. This term is shorter but less accurate than "four-stroke cycle."

was further simplified by Joseph Day in 1891. This cycle differs in principle from the four-stroke cycle in that the air-fuel charge is introduced into the cylinder under pressure at the end of the power stroke and in the brief time before the compression stroke moves any appreciable distance, as shown in Fig. 44. As the charge sweeps through the cylinder it cleans out the old products of combustion from the previous cycle in what is called cylinder scavenging. Day's simplified design used the bottom of the piston to compress the incoming charge in an enclosed crankcase as shown, and with an ingenious arrangement of intake and exhaust ports at the bottom of the cylinder he was able to eliminate the cam-operated poppet valves.

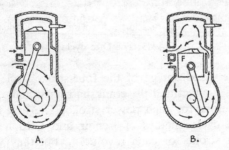

A.   B.

Fig. 44. Two-stroke cycle gasoline engine

As already mentioned, an obvious advantage of the two-stroke cycle is that there is a power stroke for every engine revolution, and thus in theory it should develop twice the power that is developed by a four-stroke cycle with the same cylinder dimensions. In actual operation, however, the efficiency is poor, since some fuel is inevitably lost with the exhaust gases during the scavenging operation. The high power-to-weight ratio has made the two-cycle engine popular with small, portable engine applications such as power lawn mowers, outboard motors, etc., where simplicity of design and low weight are more important than fuel economy.

Internal Combustion Engine Theory

To better understand the fundamentals of the internal combustion engine as a heat engine, we must turn again to the pressure-volume diagrams and the temperature-entropy diagrams of thermodynamics. In this way we can appreciate the theoretical possibilities and limitations of the engine, and get an idea of what factors must be varied to increase over-all thermal efficiency. For theoretical analysis of internal combustion engine cycles, engineers have devised the hypothetical air-standard cycle. In this cycle the cylinder contains only air, undergoing a non-flow cycle. We assume that heat can be added to, or removed from, the air in the cylinder in the same amount and with the same speed as in an actual engine when the charge is ignited in the cylinder or exhausted from the cylinder. With these assumptions, then, we can plot the air-standard Otto cycle on both pressure-volume diagrams and temperature-entropy diagrams, as shown in Fig. 45.

Let us now follow through the sequence of operation of this cycle by starting with the air at state (1) where the temperature is 70°F. and the pressure is atmospheric. First we compress the air reversibly and adiabatically to state (2), during which process the volume decreases, the pressure increases, the temperature increases, and the entropy remains constant. At this point we assume

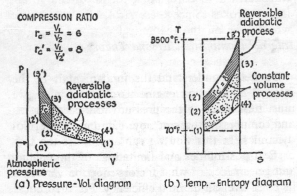

Fig. 45. Air-standard Otto cycle

that heat is added to the air instantaneously in the same amount that would be generated if a charge of gasoline vapor were suddenly ignited in the cylinder. Since this is an instantaneous process, the piston has not had time to move, and so the process 2–3 occurs at constant volume; both the pressure and temperature increase rapidly, and, since heat is being added, the entropy also increases. At state (3) the piston starts its outward stroke in a reversible adiabatic expansion to state (4), where the pressure is still somewhat above atmospheric. During the final process, 4–1, we assume that heat is removed instantaneously and at constant volume until the pressure drops back to atmospheric to complete the cycle. (This corresponds to the opening of the exhaust valve in an actual engine.) In the Otto cycle the piston next follows process 1–a and returns along the identical path a–1 to correspond to the discharge and intake strokes. Since these strokes have no effect whatsoever on the theoretical performance, they can be ignored, and the two-stroke and four-stroke cycle analysis becomes the same.[2]

In studying this cycle further, we may ask, why did we stop the compression process at state (2), and is there any theoretical advantage in continuing compression to, say, state (2') before the addition of heat (ignition)?

Before answering these questions, we should become familiar with the term called *compression ratio*. The ratio of the volume of the charge before compression (v_1) to the volume after compression (v_2) is called the compression ratio of the engine (r_c).

Expressed with symbols, $r_c = \dfrac{v_1}{v_2}$

If you recall that area on a *P-v* diagram is equal to work done, you will see that the shaded area 1–2–3–4 in Fig. 45a represents the net work of the cycle with the compression ratio of 6 to 1. Note

---

[2] Remember, though, that the four-cycle engine requires two revolutions to get one power stroke while the two-cycle engine requires only one.

also that if the compression process continues to state (2') so as to increase the compression ratio to 8 to 1, the net work of the cycle increases by an amount equal to the crosshatched area 2–2'–3'–3. Furthermore, recall that the area enclosed by a cycle on a T-S diagram (area 1–2–3–4, Fig. 45b), divided by the area representing heat added to the cycle (total area under curve 2–3), represents thermal efficiency of the cycle. Accordingly, you can see at a glance that the ratio of the shaded area 1–2–3–4, to total area under constant volume path 2–3, is less than the ratio of area 1–2'–3'–4 to the total area under constant volume path 2'–3'.

In other words, the theoretical thermal efficiency was raised by increasing the compression ratio from 6 to 8. The thermodynamic calculations to determine these theoretical efficiencies are beyond the scope of this book, but for making comparisons we can say that the thermal efficiencies might be approximately 51 per cent for the cycle shown with a compression ratio of 6 to 1, and 58 per cent for the 8 to 1 compression ratio. Remember, though, that these are theoretical efficiencies only. We should expect that any actual gasoline engine we might build on this cycle would have a somewhat lower efficiency. If it were possible to add all the heat isothermally at 3500°F. and reject all the heat isothermally at 70°F., we should have a Carnot cycle, as shown by the dotted rectangle in Fig. 45b. In this case the maximum attainable thermal efficiency can be calculated very simply, as described on page 189. (Remember that the Fahrenheit temperatures must be converted to the °F. abs. scale.) Thus:

$$\eta = \frac{3960 - 530}{3960} = 86.5\%$$

However, there is no prospect that conventional internal combustion engines will achieve thermal efficiencies of this order. In the first place, to attempt to transfer heat to or from a gas in an *isothermal* process would be impractical, particularly so for the high speeds at which these engines operate. Then too, no piston or cylinder could withstand *sustained* temperatures of 3500°F. It is true that temperatures as high as 5000°F. may occur in actual cylinders after ignition, but they exist for only the briefest fraction of a second and the cylinder has adequate time to cool down during the balance of the cycle.

There is another factor that has limited the maximum compression ratios at which the Otto cycle can operate. You can see in Fig. 45b that the temperature of the charge at the end of the compression stroke increases rapidly as the compression ratio increases. Therefore, if the compression process is carried too far, the ignition temperature of the charge is reached before the end of the stroke, causing either compression "knock" or outright failure of the cycle. This has been a limitation of all spark ignition internal-combustion engines from Otto's time to the present. However, another German engineer, born twenty-six years after Otto, was able to take this limitation and

237

turn it to advantage in a different kind of internal combustion engine.

The Diesel Cycle

Rudolf Diesel (1858–1913) was educated in Augsburg and later in Munich, where he was graduated with the highest grades in his class. In Munich he took some courses under Professor Karl von Linde, a pioneer in mechanical refrigeration and an authority in thermodynamics. Professor Linde's lectures on the low efficiency of the steam engine, as compared to the theoretical possibilities, so impressed Diesel that he could not forget them. After graduation he went to work for the Linde Ice Machine Company, first as an engineer and later as manager. One day while he was watching some ammonia compressors in an ice plant, he suddenly was impressed by the large amount of heat they gave off, and the idea of a new basic cycle came to him. It was the process that would later bear his name, in which the heat of compression alone would be used to ignite an injected fuel charge.

Diesel worked out the thermodynamics of his problem and published his results in 1893 in a paper entitled, "The Theory and Construction of a Rational Heat Motor." Basically his idea was very simple. He would compress air adiabatically to one-sixteenth of its original volume, after which the temperature would rise to about 1000°F. He would then inject fuel which would ignite automatically, without the use of an electric spark. There would be no ignition system, and the very high compression ratio would increase thermal efficiencies substantially over the Otto cycle.

As usually happens to a radically new idea, Diesel's paper was received with skepticism. Nevertheless, he managed to get permission to use the laboratory facilities of the nearby Augsburg-Nuremburg Engine Works for development of a single cylinder prototype model. When he attempted to operate this first model, it blew up with a terrific explosion, and Diesel was nearly killed, but he was successful in demonstrating that his basic idea had great merit. He obtained financial backing from the Krupp Company and went on to eliminate the initial defects of his design and produce a successful engine. In 1898 the engine was put on display in Munich, where a number of businessmen, greatly impressed with its performance, invested freely in its production. The subsequent development was something of a world-wide sensation, and Diesel made over a million dollars on his invention. It remains today an eminently successful heat engine for certain applications such as locomotives, large trucks, buses, smaller stationary power plants, etc.

The sequence of operation of the air standard Diesel cycle is shown in the P-v and T-S diagrams in Fig. 46. Air is first compressed along path 1–2 through a high compression ratio of, say, 16 to 1. Heat is then added at constant pressure, path 2–3. In the actual engine process 2–3 is accomplished by injecting fuel oil at a controlled rate, and combustion occurs due to the high temperature of the compressed air. Next, the air expands reversibly and adiabatically along path 3–4 to the end of the stroke, and, finally, heat is removed at constant volume along path 4–1. Again, in an actual engine, process 4–1 is performed by discharging the hot gases from the cylinder.

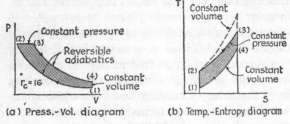

(a) Press.-Vol. diagram   (b) Temp.-Entropy diagram

Fig. 46. Air-standard Diesel cycle

Note the similarity of the Diesel cycle to the Otto cycle; the difference is in the much higher compression ratios and the constant pressure process 2–3, during which heat is added (combustion process). You can see in the temperature-entropy diagram, Fig. 46b, that if the combustion of the fuel after injection could occur at constant volume (dotted line), as in the Otto cycle, the resulting thermal efficiency would be higher. Thus the higher efficiencies of the Diesel engines over the Otto cycle engines come entirely from the much higher compression ratios that they can attain.[3] As a result, the indicated thermal efficiencies of Diesel

[3] Modern compression-ignition engines actually operate on cycles that are between the Diesel and the Otto cycles.

cycle engines are around 40 per cent, compared to around 30 per cent for Otto cycle engines.

In view of the apparent advantages, the question naturally arises, why hasn't the Diesel cycle replaced the Otto cycle in the modern automobile? Higher efficiency, lower fuel cost, and elimination of an ignition system, would all seem to be compelling reasons. There is no simple answer to this question, but it is well to remember that, important as it is, thermal efficiency is never the *sole criterion* upon which the application of a heat engine is based. The modern automobile engine is the product of a hundred years of intensive development by one of the world's largest industries. It is a marvel of reliability and dependable performance, with easy starting characteristics, in all climates and geographic conditions. No one can say that the Otto cycle gasoline engine will not be displaced some day by some superior cycle, but no one can deny either that the challenger must be formidable indeed.

Steam Turbines

A turbine may be defined as a prime mover in which a flowing fluid causes a shaft to rotate steadily in its bearings. In heat engine applications this fluid is either high velocity steam or hot gases. An elementary example of a turbine is the simple windmill. The blowing wind has kinetic[4] energy

[4] Kinetic energy is the energy stored in a body due to its velocity.

which can be transferred to the windmill. The driving force of this wind on the blades of the windmill is actually a dynamic reaction of the change of momentum of the air as it flows across the blades. This driving force causes the windmill to turn and rotate a shaft, which in turn produces power capable of doing useful work, such as pumping water from a well. The fundamental understanding of any type of turbine operation comes from an understanding of Newton's laws of motion. Much of the science of mechanics is based on these laws, and since this subject is so extensive, no attempt will be made here to explore it deeply. But so much of modern heat engine development, including steam and gas turbines, and jet and rocket engines, involves dynamic reactions of flowing fluids, that some elementary conceptual understanding of Newton's Laws is necessary if we are to discuss these heat engine types.

Newton's Third Law may be stated, "To every action there is always opposed an equal reaction." If you blow up a toy balloon and let go of it, the balloon will shoot off in one direction while the air hisses out the neck in the opposite direction. Newton's Third Law explains why. This same principle also explains why a reaction turbine wheel rotates in one direction when the wheel's high velocity nozzle lets steam or gas escape and expand in the opposite direction, or why a jet engine or rocket engine moves forward when a high velocity gas stream is ejected from its tail. But to understand exactly how much force or thrust is developed and what factors are involved in increasing or decreasing this thrust, we must turn to Newton's Second Law. This law may be stated in various ways, but we shall use this one, "A change of motion is always proportional to the motive force impressed." In other words, if we apply a force F for a time t against a mass M, its velocity will undergo a change $(\triangle V)$, in the following manner:

$$Ft = M \triangle V \quad \text{or} \quad F = \frac{M}{t} \triangle V$$

The product of force and time is called impulse; the product of mass and velocity is called momentum. Thus, if a moving fluid changes velocity, an impulse is created that is equal to the change in momentum. The equation allows us to calculate the amount of force (or thrust) developed by a moving fluid if the mass rate of flow (pounds per second) and the change in velocity (feet per second) are known. It also tells us that the force or thrust can be increased by increasing either the mass flow rate or the change in velocity. We shall be referring to these equations again a little later.

Engineers always have recognized that continuous rotation is superior to reciprocating motion in mechanical devices. There are fewer problems in vibration, lubrication, etc., and greater simplicity in design. Historical precedent also seemed to favor a rotating engine, in that Hero's little steam turbine (see Fig. 1) was the first known heat engine of ancient times. Nevertheless, the development of heat engines has followed the consistent pattern of first utilizing the reciprocating prime mover in commercially successful machines, to be followed later by turbine applications. One reason is that steam and gas turbines are essentially high-speed machines and require a sophisticated design and manufacturing technique that prior to the latter part of the 19th century were far beyond industrial capabilities.

The man who first found a need for a high-speed steam turbine, and succeeded in overcoming the difficult design problems involved, was Carl de Laval (1845–1913) of Blasenborg, Sweden. As a young man, de Laval received a fine scientific and engineering education, being graduated from the Technical University of Stockholm in 1872 with a Ph.D. degree. Well grounded in thermodynamics, he performed some early experiments with steam nozzles which were later used in sand blasting operations. His objective was to develop a nozzle that would produce the maximum steam velocity from a given steam pressure. From thermodynamic reasoning, he conceived the idea that such a nozzle must have a converging section followed by a diverging section in order to expand from high pressure down to atmospheric pressure without turbulence, in the most efficient reversible manner.

It is interesting to pause for a moment and see why this is true. If a high-pressure gas or vapor should expand through a nozzle down to atmospheric pressure without turbulence and in a reversible and adiabatic manner, we should expect that either the volume or the velocity of the gas, or both, would have to increase as the gas proceeded smoothly through the length of the nozzle. An increase in *volume* would require a progressive *increase* in cross-sectional area of the nozzle, while an increase in *velocity* would require a progressive *decrease* in cross-sectional area. Now, as these two effects are combined, the net result might be either a decrease in cross-sectional area (converging nozzle) or an increase in cross-sectional area (diverging nozzle), depending on whether velocity or volume increased at a more rapid rate. But what we actually find is this: If the initial pressure is high enough, there must be a *converging channel* in the fore part of the nozzle, and then, as the pressure drops to a *critical pressure,* at a point in the *nozzle throat,* there is a reversal in the relative rates of velocity and volume increases, and a *diverging channel* is needed in the after part of the nozzle. So we have the so-called converging-diverging nozzle with the characteristic shape shown in Fig. 47. The ratio of the critical pressure to the initial pressure, called the critical pressure ratio, is .528 for air and about .57 for steam.

A unique feature in the flow of gases through nozzles is that the velocity reached by the gas *in the throat* can never exceed the velocity of sound in the gas. This velocity varies with the kind and state of the gas, but is around 1100 feet per second for air at ordinary room conditions. Thus, if some application of gas flow is desired with maximum velocities higher than sonic velocities, an interesting problem in thermodynamics is involved, and very careful nozzle design and manufacture are necessary. A converging-diverging nozzle profile is drawn from theoretical computations to ensure the closest possible approach to a reversible adiabatic process in which there is the maximum conversion of internal energy to kinetic energy in the high-velocity exhaust gas stream. If any actual nozzle, whether for turbine nozzle or rocket engine application, is not constructed with precision according to this prescribed form, excessive turbulence and fluid friction occur, and they in turn cause irreversibility and loss of available energy.

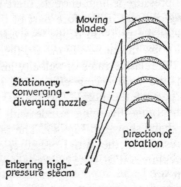

Fig. 47. De Laval nozzle and impulse turbine blades

This, then, was the problem that young de Laval was working on when he developed his sand blasting machine. One day he happened to have his nozzles set in such a way that the reactive force of each one complemented the others, and he was astonished to find that a full application of steam caused the entire machine to rotate. He was so impressed by the force of this reaction that it remained in the back of his mind for many years and later led to one of his greatest inventions, the impulse steam turbine.

This invention came in 1882 when de Laval was searching for some new high-speed prime mover to operate his newly-invented cream separator. The separator required extremely high rotative speeds that were difficult to obtain with conventional gear trains that were power-consuming and noisy. What de Laval wanted was some kind of driving engine that could be directly connected, and he solved his problem by inventing the single-stage impulse turbine, Fig. 47.

The impulse turbine operates on the same principle as the windmill, except, of course, that it is designed and manufactured with much greater precision for the highest possible efficiency. High-pressure steam is sent through stationary converging-diverging nozzles and discharged at very high velocity against the moving blades of the turbine wheel. Let us work a little problem to see what happens. Suppose the initial steam velocity is 2000 feet per second and suppose also that the blades of the turbine are moving at a velocity of 1000 feet per second. Then the velocity of the *entering* steam relative to the moving blades would be 2000 – 1000 or 1000 feet per second. Then if the direction of the steam were completely reversed by the moving blades, the velocity of the *leaving* steam would be 1000 – 1000 or *zero*, relative to the nozzle and casing. In other words all the kinetic energy of the steam would be converted to work produced by the turning turbine wheel.

This essentially is a description of de Laval's turbine. He wanted high speeds and he certainly got them. In fact, his first experimental models gave him trouble with exploding turbine wheels from the high stresses and uncontrolled vibration encountered at speeds up to 40,000 rpm. He overcame this difficulty with the daring concept of the flexible shaft, which allowed the wheels to seek their own center of rotation. Aside from cream separators, however, most steam turbine applications do not require such high rotative speeds. De Laval attempted to obtain moderate rotative speeds with the invention of a helical reducing gear. A number of his turbines were sold and used in commercial service for driving electric generators. But, as already mentioned, reduction gears of this magnitude are generally impractical, and other more efficient ways were soon found to accomplish the same results. One approach was to employ a design called velocity staging, or Curtis staging, in honor of Charles Gordon Curtis, the engineer who introduced it in the United States in 1898. To see how this works let us examine Fig. 48.

Suppose the steam again entered the first wheel or stage with a velocity of 2000 feet per second. But now the turbine has two moving wheels fastened to a common shaft, each with a blade velocity of only 500 feet per second. The entering steam velocity relative to the first stage would now be 2000 − 500, or 1500 feet per second, and upon reversing its direction it would leave the first stage at 1500 – 500, or 1000 feet per second relative to the turbine casing. The steam now would be reversed again by a row of *stationary* blades, as shown, and thus would enter the second stage at a velocity of 1000 – 500, or 500 feet per second relative to the moving blades. A final reversal of

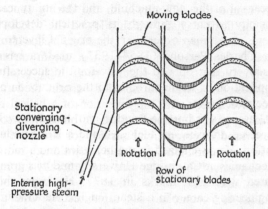

Fig. 48. Impulse turbine with two velocity stages

direction in the second stage would cause the steam to leave the wheel at 500 – 500, or zero velocity relative to the turbine casing. Thus the two stages would cut the turbine speed to one quarter of the entering steam velocity but still utilize all the steam's kinetic energy. Velocity staging, however, can be used only within limits as an effective means of reducing turbine speeds. Because of the extremely high steam velocities developed, the friction and turbulence losses are excessive if more than two stages are employed. For still more efficient speed reduction other methods can be used, as we shall soon see.

Today the steam turbine has almost displaced the steam engine as a prime mover in the production of power. And again, as in the case of the steam engine and the internal combustion engine, the man who had the inspiration to see the great potential of this new machine, and the ability and tenacity to carry through its practical development, was a man other than the original inventor. Sir Charles Parsons (1854–1931) made a basic discovery that opened the way for the successful application of steam turbines to the production of electrical power.

Parsons was born in London and, like de Laval, received an excellent technical and scientific education. He specialized in mathematics and applied mechanics at Cambridge University and was graduated with high marks in 1877. He began his engineering career in a steam engine manufacturing company, and in 1881 he developed and patented a four-cylinder high-speed epicycloidal steam engine. Advancing rapidly, Parsons soon acquired a junior partnership in an electric dynamo company, where he worked on a steam engine that could operate dynamos by direct drive. He soon realized that he needed higher rotative speeds than steam engines could supply, and around 1884 he began a study of steam turbine design. It was during this study that he made a basic discovery. The idea occurred to him that he could reduce the speed of the de Laval turbine by placing a number of turbine wheels on a single shaft. Parsons reasoned that each wheel could exhaust steam to some lower pressure into succeeding compartments, with the net result of reducing the speed at which the turbine must operate. He then went on to develop a successful prototype model.

This concept, known as *pressure staging,* requires that each turbine wheel be contained in a separate compartment sealed from the others by a close-tolerance, thin-edge diaphragm at the rotating shaft. This diaphragm prevents steam from leaking from one compartment to the next except through the nozzles, where you want it. Fig. 49 is a cross-sectional view of a typical multistage turbine that illustrates not only pressure staging but velocity staging as well. In this model the first wheel utilizes two velocity stages, which in turn are followed by seven successive pressure stages.

Parsons did his research and development work very thoroughly, and his turbines were immediately successful. He next developed a turbine type in which the moving blades, as well as the fixed nozzles, were formed into nozzle shapes, and thus the torque or turning force on the turbine wheel came primarily from the reaction of steam issuing from the moving nozzles.[5] Turbines of this type can also be adapted to pressure staging, and multistage reaction turbines have come to be known as the Parsons type.

So great was the potential for turbogeneration

[5] This was the same principle upon which Hero's aeolipile operated, Fig. 1.

of electric power that Parsons lived to see the turbine replace the reciprocating steam engine altogether in the large central-station power plants. The units he manufactured increased in size from 7½ kilowatts in 1884 to 200,000 kilowatts in 1931, at the time of his death. Although Parsons remained a leading manufacturer of steam turbines, many other companies in both Europe and

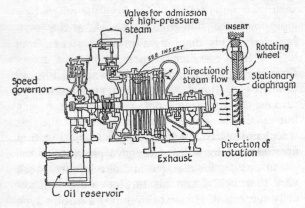

Fig. 49. Multistage impulse turbine

America were soon working in the field. Many different turbine types were developed, but the concept of pressure compounding remained basic. Curtis staging, Parsons staging, Rateau staging, and various combinations of the three became competitive types. Rateau staging was named for Camille Rateau, a French engineer who contributed much to the development of multistage de Laval-type turbines using Parsons' pressure-staging principle. Further classifications were made in regard to the flow of steam through the unit. An example of a giant tandem triple-flow unit is shown in Fig. 50 to give an idea of the great size to which modern steam turbines can be built today.

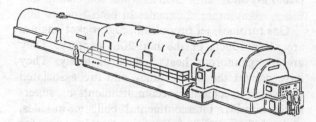

Fig. 50. Scale model of outdoor tandem triple-flow steam turbine generator unit with geared exciter

Approximately 80 per cent of all electric power generated in the United States now comes from steam turbine plants.[6] Over-all thermal efficiencies have been steadily increasing, from less than 7 per cent in 1900 to approximately 38 per cent in the most efficient plants of today. The size of turbo-generating plants also has continued to increase since Parsons' day. Several units over 300 megawatts[7] are now in operation, and a 600 megawatt unit was under construction in 1960. Steam temperatures of 1200°F. and pressures of 5000 psia are being planned, in the unending search for higher thermal efficiencies. But regardless of how massive and complex these giant steam turbine

[6] Most of the balance comes from hydroelectric stations.
[7] one megawatt = 1000 kilowatts = 1,000,000 watts

applications become, we know that they are basically a simple heat engine operating on the Rankine cycle (with modifications) and subject to the inexorable limitation of the Carnot Principle.

Gas Turbines

Gas turbines, jet propulsion, and rocket engines are all products of the mid-20th century. They are the glamorous heat engines of today. They have caught the public fancy and are associated with such spectacular accomplishments as supersonic aircraft, intercontinental ballistic missiles, and orbiting satellites. These heat engines are, for the most part, internal combustion engines, and, as was the case with the steam turbine, they have followed the previously successful development of their reciprocating engine counterparts. Continuous rotation and steady flow of the working medium, as compared to reciprocating action, is even more desirable in internal combustion heat engines than in steam engines. The source of many design and operating difficulties in reciprocating piston-type engines is traceable to the interruptable ignition and cyclic fuel supply. Nevertheless, development of gas turbines lagged, primarily because of the high gas temperature involved, and it was not until 1902 that an experimental gas turbine was built that actually could run. S. A. Moss, as a graduate student at Cornell University, converted a de Laval steam turbine for this purpose, and, although his turbine did run after a fashion, it could not develop enough power to operate the compressor that supplied it with combustion air. In 1905 two Frenchman, Armengand and Lemale, constructed a successful gas turbine that consisted of a two-stage impulse turbine driving a Rateau multistaged centrifugal compressor. The compressor supplied high-pressure air to a combustion chamber where fuel was burned, and the resulting high-temperature, high-pressure gases were then sent through a turbine wheel. An attempt was made to cope with the high-combustion temperatures by cooling the turbine blades and discs with water. The machine delivered power, but the thermal efficiency was an unexciting 3 per cent.

So much for a brief look into the history of the gas turbine. In its early development period it was no competition for either the steam turbine or the reciprocating internal combustion engine, but certain recent significant advances in the knowledge of materials may change the picture. Before we discuss this further, let us pause for a moment and examine the basic cycle and flow diagram on which the gas turbine operates. In this way we can get an understanding of the thermodynamic capabilities and limitations of this new heat engine type.

Basically the gas turbine is a very simple power plant. It consists of an air compressor, a combustion chamber, and a turbine arranged in some manner similar to that shown in Fig. 51. Atmospheric air enters the multistage turbocompressor, where it is compressed to anywhere from 50 to

80 psia. It then is discharged into a combustion chamber, where fuel is introduced and burned continuously, as in a furnace. The heated air, together with the products of combustion, are then expanded through the turbine back to atmospheric pressure. At this point the exhaust air and gases, which are still at a relatively high temperature, can either be exhausted directly to the atmosphere, as shown in Fig. 51, or be sent back

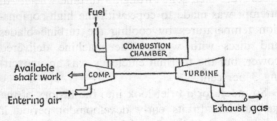

Fig. 51. Flow diagram for a simple gas turbine power plant

through a heat exchanger to preheat the air leaving the compressor and entering the combustion chamber. This latter arrangement, called regeneration, complicates the design somewhat but can substantially increase the efficiency by reducing the fuel consumption. The compressor and turbine can be connected to a common shaft, and the excess power developed by the turbine over the power required by the compressor (usually less than half), is delivered as available shaft work. This shaft can be connected to some useful load, such as a generator or a propeller on an airplane.

For reasons previously discussed, the analysis

of the gas turbine cycle is simplified by constructing an ideal air-standard gas-turbine cycle,[8] as shown in Fig. 52. Recall that in air-standard cycles we assume that air alone is used as the working medium in a closed system (that is, it never leaves the engine). We also assume that we can

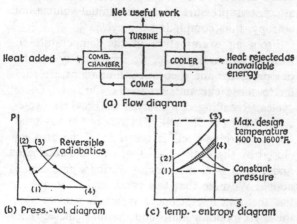

(a) Flow diagram

(b) Press.-vol. diagram   (c) Temp. - entropy diagram

Fig. 52. The simple air-standard gas-turbine cycle

add heat to this air in the same amount as that generated by burning a gas mixture in an actual engine. Furthermore, we assume that heat can be removed from the air with some cooling device in the same amount that heat is rejected from an actual engine when the hot gases are expelled from the exhaust ports.

With these assumptions, then, let us trace through the cycle. Air enters the compressor at

[8] Sometimes called the Joule cycle or the Brayton cycle.

state (1) where it is compressed reversibly and adiabatically (constant entropy) to state (2). Heat is then added at constant pressure, and the temperature rises rapidly to the maximum allowable design temperature at state (3). The air then is expanded reversibly and adiabatically to the initial pressure, state (4), after which it is cooled at constant pressure back to its initial volume and entropy, thus completing the cycle.

From an examination of the temperature-entropy diagram, Fig. 52c, we immediately see that our problems and theoretical limitations are similar to those encountered in the Otto and Diesel cycles. Recalling our analysis of previous cycles, we see that the thermal efficiency of the air-standard gas turbine cycle is the ratio of the area enclosed by the cycle, 1–2–3–4, over the total area under path 2–3, the process during which heat is added. We note that this ratio, and consequently the theoretical efficiency, is much smaller than the corresponding ratio and thermal efficiency for the Carnot cycle, shown as the rectangle completed with dotted lines. This discrepancy exists because the transfer of heat during the two constant pressure processes departs greatly from the isothermal processes required by the reversible Carnot cycle. Note, however, that the constant pressure path 1–4 is a flatter curve than the constant volume path for the Diesel or Otto cycles, and consequently we theoretically gain the small amount of work shown by the crosshatched triangle in Fig. 52c.

The critical factor in the gas turbine cycle is

the temperature developed at state (3), where 1400°F. to 1600°F. represents the highest permissible values in even the best current designs. As stated earlier, reciprocating gasoline engines can tolerate substantially higher temperatures than this only because the temperatures occur periodically and exist for such a brief moment. In gas turbines, on the other hand, combustion is continuous, and the combustion chamber, passages to the turbine, and the first stage of turbine blades all are constantly exposed to this peak temperature, indicated by state (3). A common method of controlling this high temperature is to supply excess air through the compressor to dilute the products of combustion to the required design temperature. Unfortunately, this dilution not only lowers the Carnot efficiency but also increases the power losses since more air must be compressed than the amount theoretically needed.

In recent years there has been intensive research to find materials that can maintain strength and wearing properties at these extremely high temperatures. This research has followed two lines, cemented hard carbides and ceramics. Cemented carbides, manufactured by a technique called powder metallurgy, are made from carbides of tungsten, zirconium, molybdenum, tantalum, and titanium, with cobalt as a matrix or binding material. Laboratory tests show that these materials can withstand temperatures up to 1800°F. and even higher. Ceramic materials under investigation include porcelain, fused quartz, and sintered aluminum with iron, but many unsolved problems remain.

At the present time over-all thermal efficiencies are rather poor as compared with piston-type internal combustion engines (see Fig. 53). It would be helpful, of course, if still more efficient axial compressors and turbine wheels could be developed, but the most promising prospect seems to lie in the development of higher temperature materials, more effective methods of cooling the turbine disc and blades, and further refinements in the regenerative-type processes discussed earlier.

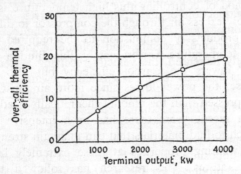

Fig. 53. Performance of a 4000-kilowatt stationary gas turbine power plant

Thermal efficiency is never the only factor to be considered, and even at the present state of development the future of the gas turbine is assured. It is being used in certain types of central station work, offers great promise in railway locomotives, and is particularly well suited for aircraft application, as we shall see next. The gas turbine is being studied for automobiles and trucks, and some prototype models have been built and tested.

Jet Propulsion

As previously mentioned, jet propulsion is a consequence of Newton's Third Law of Motion. It occurs when the engine undergoes a forward thrust while ejecting a fluid stream rearward. In jet-turbine engines, Fig. 54, or turbojets as they are often called, air enters the compressor intake at some initial velocity, and then through the combined action of the compressor (driven by the turbine wheel) and the combustion chamber, the temperature, pressure, and volume of the air are vastly increased, the velocity receiving a tremendous boost as the air is ejected rearward.

This increase in velocity of the hot gases passing through the exhaust nozzle is produced by a force or action to which there must be a corresponding reaction. This reactive force, acting in the opposite direction, is the thrust or propulsive force produced by the engine. We can evaluate this force numerically by calculating the rate of change of momentum of the gas stream flowing steadily through the engine. Let us work a simple example to see how this thrust can be calculated. Suppose we have a jet engine that draws in 100 pounds of air per second, and after first compressing it and then heating it in the combustion chamber, ejects it rearward with a total *increase* in velocity of 1500 feet per second. The thrust de-

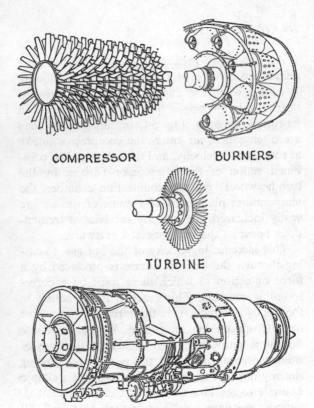

COMPRESSOR   BURNERS

TURBINE

Fig. 54. Typical turbojet engine

262

veloped can be calculated with the impulse-momentum equation shown on page 243, as follows:

$$F = \frac{M}{t}\Delta V$$

where F = *thrust*

$\frac{M}{t}$ = mass *per second*

ΔV = *change in velocity in feet per second*

Since mass M is related to weight W and gravitational acceleration in the following manner, $M = \frac{W}{32.2}$, we can rewrite the above equation as follows:

$$F = \frac{W}{32.2t}\Delta V$$

where $\frac{W}{t}$ *is now pounds weight per second.*

Then, $F = \frac{100}{32.2} \times 1500$

$= 4660$ *pounds of thrust.*

This equation also tells us that the thrust could be doubled to 9320 pounds force either by doubling the weight of air to 200 pounds per second, or by doubling the increase in velocity to 3000 feet per second.

The performance characteristics of the jet engine make it a superb heat engine for high-altitude, high-speed aircraft, as we shall presently see. It has remarkable simplicity of design, it can burn the cheapest fuel, it is light in weight, virtually vibration-free, and its high rotative speeds permit it to handle easily the enormous volumes of thin air required for high-altitude operation.

Historically, the development of jet propulsion in conjunction with useful heat engines is of very recent origin. Proposals for jet aircraft were advanced in the years following World War I, but the first successful flight was not made until 1940. In that year the Caproni Company of Italy reported an airplane flight operated on this principle. Experimentation and development of jet propulsion were greatly stimulated by military requirements in World War II, with Germany making the most significant progress.

Thermodynamically, the turbojet engine still follows the air-standard gas-turbine cycle, Fig. 52, but now there is no available net shaft work since all the energy of the turbine goes into operation of the compressor. Instead, the useful work of the turbojet engine results from the thrust produced against the airplane mass itself. This work is used not only in overcoming the drag of air friction against the various surfaces, but in storing a considerable percentage directly in the airplane in bringing the craft to its high velocity (kinetic energy) and in lifting it to the great elevations (potential energy) at which jet aircraft fly. This stored energy is recovered, of course, as the airplane again descends to earth.

We mentioned that jet engines have certain advantages in high-flying aircraft applications. One is that the thermal efficiency of a jet engine actually *increases* as the air speed of the airplane increases. How is this possible? A phenomenon known as *ram effect* is the explanation. As the forward motion of the airplane increases, there is a natural build-up of air pressure at the engine intake. This build-up is called ram pressure, and it continues to increase with further increases in airplane speed. Since the function of the compressor (see Fig. 54) is to compress the air prior to combustion, this ram pressure is a welcome bonus

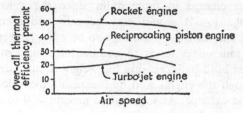

Fig. 55. Changes in aircraft engine efficiency with air speed

which costs the engine nothing. The net result is that both the weight of air being accelerated through the engine and the jet velocity are increased at no additional compressor power requirements. Both of these increases, as we have seen, increase thrust, with the result that thermal efficiencies increase with increased air speed. This is illustrated in Fig. 55. Piston-type reciprocating engines are not designed to take advantage of this ram pressure, and because of other characteristics their efficiency decreases with increased air speed.

There is another advantageous effect of ram pressure insofar as it affects the thrust developed by the jet engine. As a turbojet moves forward from a stationary position, it naturally tends to lose thrust due to its increasing forward velocity. We can see this clearly by examining again the thrust equation,

$$F = \frac{W}{32.2t} \times \triangle V$$

If the forward velocity of the aircraft is increased until it equals the velocity of the jet exhaust, there is no change in momentum since the velocity change ($\triangle V$) would now be zero and accordingly the thrust (F) would also be zero. However, the ram effect tends to compensate this loss of thrust both by increasing the weight of air passing through the engine and by increasing the velocity of the exhaust. At some speed around 450 to 500 miles per hour (varying with the airplane) this ram pressure increases to the point where it fully compensates for the thrust lost in increase of velocity. In fact, if the air speed is high enough, the compressor, and consequently the turbine, can be eliminated altogether, in which case we have a ram-jet engine. Such speeds, however, are beyond the operating limits of present-day commercial aircraft; furthermore, the ram-jet engine has the obvious disadvantage of zero thrust at zero air speed and needs some auxiliary method to bring it up to operating range. Still, it is interesting to note that this type of heat engine is used in the Navajo long-range missile, the Bomarc interceptor missile, and the Talos missile, where air speeds over 1500 miles per hour are achieved.

Another variation of the turbojet engine is the turboprop. In the operation of this engine large volumes of air are first compressed by a multi-stage, axial flow turbocompressor, then passed through a combustion chamber and into a turbine section, similar to the process shown in Fig. 54. Here the design differs, however, in that excess turbine capacity is provided to rotate a *propeller* in addition to the compressor. Because of this additional large power requirement, only a small amount of energy is left over for pure jet propulsion. However, ram effect can be used to help increase efficiency, just as in the pure turbojet.

From the standpoint of ideal thermodynamic cycle analysis there is no difference between the turboprop and turbojet cycles. They differ only in the manner in which useful work is extracted from the cycle. Experience has shown that the turbo-prop engine is ideally suited for airplanes of intermediate size and speed where the advantages of both gas turbine and propeller operation can be effectively utilized.

Rocket Engines

Although there are records of military use of crude rockets centuries ago, for signaling and pyrotechnic displays, an intelligent understanding of their construction and control has come about only in the last fifty years. Dr. Robert H. Goddard (1882–1945), American physicist, stood out among early investigators doing theoretical and experimental research on the basic concepts of rocket propulsion. A report by Goddard, published by the Smithsonian Institution in 1919, was the first scientific publication on the subject.

A rocket engine can be defined in a general way as an apparatus that develops thrust solely by ejecting matter from within the vehicle it propels. It differs from the turbojet type of engine in that there is no air induction system; all the reactants are contained within the body of the rocket itself. Thus the rocket engine, among all internal-combustion engine types, is unique in that its operation is independent of the earth's atmosphere.

A rocket engine, as a thermodynamic heat engine, is an apparatus for converting the heat energy released from burning some fuel or propellant with self-contained oxidizer, into the kinetic energy of a high-velocity exhaust jet, Fig. 56. The reaction to this high-velocity jet is the rocket thrust. The fuel may be a liquid such as gasoline, alcohol, liquid ammonia, or hydrazine, with a liquid oxidizer such as liquid oxygen or nitric acid. It may be a solid, of complex chemical composition, formulated by companies specializing in this field. Solid rocket fuels must also carry their own oxidizer, such as potassium perchlorate, mixed and cast with the fuel into usable shapes.

The rocket engine is also unique among heat engines in that it does not operate on a cycle. How is this compatible with Carnot's concept that all useful heat engines must operate in a cyclic manner? The explanation is that Carnot was referring to a *continuously operating* heat engine.

The rocket engine, of course, does not act continuously. When the propellant charge is used up, usually in a matter of seconds or minutes at the most, it has no further use, and, like a rifle shell cartridge, is discarded.

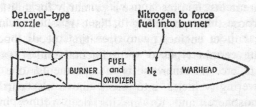

Fig. 56. Schematic diagram of ballistic missile equipped with rocket engine

For this reason, any attempt to analyze rocket performance on the basis of the Carnot criterion may not have much meaning. We could charge the work of compression of a liquid propellant to the performance of the rocket engine, in which case the open gas-turbine or Brayton cycle would be the ideal cycle for reference purposes. However, it is customary to define the thermal efficiency of a rocket engine as the ratio of its instantaneous power of thrust to the rate at which the propellant energy is being used.

By whatever standards thermal efficiency of rockets is judged, though, the maximum capabilities will be high (see Fig. 55), because the operating gas temperatures can be extremely high (4000°F. to 5000°F.). This temperature is possible because the design of the engine is exceedingly simple, and its required life is exceedingly short.

How important is the rocket engine as a source of power in the world today? Notwithstanding its glamour and widespread publicity, it supplies only an infinitesimal part of our present energy requirements. Its present use is primarily for military purposes, for propelling ballistic missiles, bringing ram-jet engines up to operating speeds, operating certain types of experimental military aircraft, etc. Its other use is the spectacular one of powering vehicles into orbit above the earth's atmosphere, and for making deep probes into outer space. In this respect, however, it is of the greatest importance to the adventurous spirit of man, for it is the only engine known that has the proved capability of propelling a payload beyond the earth's gravitational field.

EPILOGUE

In concluding our story on heat engines it would be well to examine briefly the entire power-producing capabilities and resources of the world today. In this way we can better place the heat engine in perspective, and so better appreciate its past development, present position, and its outlook for the future.

All mechanical and electrical power on earth comes from stored energy reserves. Some of this energy is stored *mechanical* energy such as water and wind. This stored mechanical energy is very high-grade because, at least in theory, it can be converted entirely into useful work by a perfect turbine. Wind power has had its day and now supplies only an insignificant percentage of our power needs, and there is little prospect that this will change. Water power is one of the world's oldest energy sources and remains a significant source of potential mechanical energy. It is harnessed primarily by damming natural waterways and then using the resulting head of water to operate hydraulic turbines for producing electrical power. At present about 20 per cent of the electrical power generated in the United States is produced in this way, and it is estimated that there still remains an undeveloped potential of about 90 million kilowatts. In some countries, Canada and Switzerland among them, hydroelectric power accounts for a greater percentage.

By far the most important source of stored energy in the world up to the present day, however, has been the *chemical* energy in the so-called fossil fuels. These are the coal, oil, and gas reserves stored in the earth's crust. Combustion releases this energy in the form of heat, and as such it is a relatively low grade of energy and consequently more difficult to convert into useful work or power. When these fuels are burned at temperatures around 3000°F. to 4000°F., a high-temperature heat-energy reservoir is created from which heat engines can operate. As we have seen, these heat engines, even when perfect, cannot convert all the heat into work, but are subject to the theoretical limitations of the Carnot cycle. We do not know the exact percentage of world power produced in this way, but it is very high. For instance, about 80 per cent of all electrical power produced in the United States comes from steam turbine generators alone. Then, too, we know that the total horsepower produced by all classes of internal combustion engines for stationary service and for powering locomotives, automobiles, and airplanes is enormous.

Because our very civilization depends on them, we must face the fact that these fossil fuels are a diminishing reserve. Although in ample supply at present, they ultimately will become scarce—this is certain. What, then, is the future of the heat engine? There are, of course, additional sources of chemical combustion other than the fossil fuels. For instance, oxygen-hydrogen, oxygen-aluminum, and hydrogen-fluorine mixtures all produce flames at temperatures much higher than the fossil fuels, but the catch is that they are not available in nature in a readily usable form. Too much work must be expended to produce them to permit their economical use in heat engines. There are exceptions, such as rocket engines, where the necessity of using high-performance exotic fuels justifies the higher cost.

Another potential source of heat energy is the energy stored in the atom. Both nuclear fission and fusion have been achieved by man, and nuclear fission can now be controlled with sufficient precision to supply heat for operating heat engines. There is hope that controlled thermonuclear fusion may become a reality some day as another great reservoir of power, and intensive research is being directed toward this end. Up to the present time atomic power plants have operated on conventional steam power cycles with steam turbines as the prime movers and nuclear reactors serving as the heat source for the boilers. However, other types of nuclear powered heat engines will inevitably be developed. For example, there is now (1961) under construction a 22,600 horsepower gas turbine heat engine in which the working medium will be helium, circulated directly through a helium-cooled reactor and used directly in a gas turbine. It is estimated that the thermal efficiency of this helium gas turbine cycle will be 31 per cent.

Still another source of heat energy is the sun. The earth's atmosphere receives about 420 Btu of thermal radiation per hour for every square foot of area pointed toward the sun. Over an acre of ground this energy reception is nearly equivalent to burning one ton of coal per hour. If we utilized only one per cent of our available ground area for solar power plants, we would have a theoretical capability of producing far more power than all the steam and hydroelectric power plants in the world today. Furthermore, this source of heat is eternal, at least insofar as the destiny of man is concerned. Why aren't we using it? The answer lies in the great difficulty of gathering and concentrating this energy so it can be used economically in heat engines. Although we have the technical know-how to produce power from solar energy today, it is not competitive with other systems. Only future events will determine whether this permanent energy source will be widely used for this purpose.

Thus we see that sources of heat energy are still abundant in the world today, and there is every prospect that the conventional heat engines that we have read about in this book will continue to dominate the production of power for some time to come. But engineers and scientists, in their restless search for more and cheaper power, for power in small lightweight packages that will give dependable, service-free operation for long periods of time, and for power to supply the unique requirements of space vehicles, are on the verge of exciting new technological breakthroughs. New, fundamentally different types of power systems are being proposed with strange-sounding names. One called *magnetohydrodynamics* continues to use the principle of the heat engine cycle, but works with extremely high-temperature and high-velocity gases in an area of physics called plasma dynamics. Theoretical calculations show that in this type of system thermal efficiencies in the order of 60 per cent are entirely feasible.

Two other power-producing devices now under investigation involve *thermoelectric* and *thermoionic* generators. These devices have the capability of converting heat energy directly into electrical energy. Efficiencies at present, in the small experimental laboratory models, are about 6 per cent. These are quite low percentages, but they have an important advantage of remaining essentially constant for all sizes of machines. Thus, for very small capacity machines they are competitive now with the efficiencies of conventional heat engines of comparable size, and predictions are being made that the 6 per cent efficiency will increase to 20 per cent by 1970.

Another basically different type of engine now undergoing intensive development is the *fuel cell*. This is fundamentally an electric battery, using inexpensive fuels that are continuously fed into the system while it is operating. The use of a battery to produce electrical and mechanical power is not new. Furthermore, the battery has the most appealing advantage of converting stored chemical energy directly into work, without the theoretical restrictions of the heat engine cycle. Unfortunately, however, low-temperature batteries or fuel cells require expensive materials in their operation and so far have had a very limited use in the production of power. High-temperature fuel cells, on the other hand, can be operated with low-cost materials, but at the present time external heat must be added to sustain their operation. There are formidable problems to be overcome also, particularly regarding the corrosion of materials. Here too, though, efficiencies are independent of the size of the fuel cell, and if development difficulties can be overcome, we should have fuel cell engines of modest size commercially available in a few years with efficiencies nearly twice that of conventional heat engines.

No one can predict with certainty what type of power-producing machines we may have in the distant future, but it is inevitable that continued progress will be made. Reflecting on the progress made in the last century, we consistently find the thread of physics interwoven in the heat engine story. In the earlier years it was not uncommon to find physicists of world renown working on problems and writing technical papers directly concerned with heat engines, at least the more theoretical and fundamental aspects of their operation. In later years the contributions of the physicists were just as great, but now they were more indirect in that they supplied the framework around which the engineering sciences grew. These sciences included thermodynamics, heat transfer, statics, dynamics, fluid mechanics, and other subjects that now provide the indispensable theoretical knowledge the young mechanical engineer must have to carry on in this field. Nor is the end of this trend in sight. As the physicists unfold more and more of the mysteries of matter and physical phenomena about us, the engineering sciences continue to broaden and new ones continue to emerge. Currently, new knowledge in solid state physics is deepening our insight in the field of metallurgy, and a new engineering area of materials science seems to be emerging.

An educational phenomenon of the past decade is the speed with which engineering curricula are being oriented toward pure science. The knowledge, training, and skill of future engineering graduates will merge ever closer with the similar attributes of their physicist colleagues. And because of this trend we find that the lead time between a breakthrough in pure science and its exploitation in the practical hardware of the engineer is becoming shorter and shorter. Progress in heat engine development is proving to be no exception to this trend.

There does seem to be an exception, however, to the historical precedent that great engineering achievements were often the result of the work of a single genius. It is highly improbable that any future heat engine revolution will be credited to a single man in the way that Watt, Otto, Diesel, and Sir Charles Parsons are identified today. It is more likely that such advances will come from highly organized research and development organizations in which teams of engineers and scientists pool their specialized knowledge for a more powerful and efficient attack on the problem. The teams will have the resources and facilities of government and great corporations behind them. An example of this approach is the present massive effort behind the incredibly complex design of rocket engines and vehicles for space travel. In this case the resources of the Federal government itself are required to sustain the effort.

Meanwhile, the thirst for power throughout the world continues to grow at an astonishing rate, and the role of physics will continue to be a dominant one in the saga of the heat engine in the years to come. This will be true not only because of spectacular scientific breakthroughs which can be exploited by heat engine developers and designers, but also because physics will ever be the cornerstone in the technical education of young engineers.

APPENDIX

Proof of the Carnot Principle

A formal statement of the Carnot Principle is as follows:

> *Of all heat engines receiving heat from the same constant temperature source and rejecting heat to the same constant temperature receiver, none can be more efficient than a reversible engine.*

We prove this by a rather backhanded, though perfectly valid, method. The general approach is to assume that the principle is false—that is, that there is an engine more efficient than a reversible engine—and then show that such an assumption violates the Second Law of Thermodynamics.

Referring to Fig. 57, suppose that we have two heat engines, both operating between the same heat source and receiver. One is a reversible engine R while the other is engine X with an assumed efficiency higher than engine R. This can be stated with mathematical symbols as follows:

$$\eta_X > \eta_R \underline{\qquad}(1)$$

Now let the engines operate in such a manner that the work output (W) of both is identical,

279

$$W_X = W_R \quad \text{------------(2)}$$

If now we divide equality (2) by inequality (1) we get,

$$\frac{W_X}{\eta_X} < \frac{W_R}{\eta_R} \quad \text{------------(3)}$$

But thermal efficiency (η) by definition is equal to work output (W) over heat input (Q), thus,

$$\eta = \frac{W}{Q} \quad \text{------------(4)}$$

Then rearranging and substituting (4) in (3) we have,

$$Q_X < Q_R \quad \text{------------(5)}$$

Since these engines are operating in cycles, where the working fluids periodically return to their initial state, there cannot be any accumulation of stored energy in the system, and therefore the First Law of Thermodynamics tells us that all the heat *added* (Q) must be accounted for by

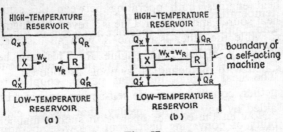

Fig. 57.

either heat (Q') or work (W) *leaving* the system, thus,

$$Q_X = W_X + Q'_X$$

or $\qquad Q'_X = Q_X - W_X$ _____ (6)

also, $\qquad Q_R = W_R + Q'_R$

or $\qquad Q'_R = Q_R - W_R$ _____ (7)

Now let us subtract equality (2) from inequality (5), then,

$$Q_X - W_X < Q_R - W_R \qquad (8)$$

Next, substituting equations (6) and (7) into equation (8) we have,

$$Q'_X < Q'_R \qquad\qquad (9)$$

Now by definition, a reversible engine can reverse its operation, simply by changing the direction of Q_R, W_R, and Q'_R. Let us now do this but keep the magnitude of the work and heat terms the same as before. Note that we now have a *heat pump* in which work is put into the heat engine operating in reverse, and heat is pumped out of the low-temperature reservoir and into the high-temperature reservoir. And since $W_X = W_R$, we can couple the shafts together as shown in Fig. 57 and let engine X drive heat pump R.

What is the net result of this new arrangement? The heat engine and heat pump, coupled together, constitute a single self-acting machine, unaided by any external agency, that has the capability of conveying heat from a low-temperature reservoir to a higher temperature reservoir.[1] This is inconceivable since it violates the Clausius statement of the Second Law of Thermodynamics (see page 86). Therefore, we must conclude that our original assumption, that some engine can have an efficiency higher than a reversible engine, is inadmissible, and thus the Carnot Principle is proved.

[1] This is true since $Q'X < Q'R$ and $QX < QR$.

INDEX

Italic page numbers indicate main entries.

ANCHOR BOOKS

SCIENCE STUDY SERIES

B-382
5-15